Chapter I

Future Cities and Sustainable Development

Significance and Practice of the UN Sustainable Development Agenda for the Inter-city Cooperation

Yu Hongyuan
Director of Institute for Public Policy of Shanghai
Institutes for International Studies

This is an excerpt from the author's speech at the "2023 Shanghai-Espoo Sustainable Development Forum".

The white paper titled "A Global Community of Shared Future: China's Proposals and Actions" released by the People's Republic of China mentioned that a community with shared future for mankind needs common values. Where does this common value come from? Sustainable development in world cities is an important common value.

Every city, every person in a city, every "Shanghai Manual" and every case in it are the participants, sharers and creators of common human values. All knowledge is practically local, especially in the area of sustainable development. In the sustainable development construction project of the United Nations (UN), we are participants, contributors and builders. This is sustainable knowledge. No country can monopolize the discourse power of sustainable development. Everyone and every city are creators, which is also an important solid foundation for World Cities Day in Shanghai to achieve such a huge impact on the world.

Policies, funds and actions are very important in the UN sustainable development agenda. We need a variety of policies, whether from international or domestic sources, to provide a signal to guide the flow of funds. In the fields of infrastructure, environmental engineering, climate change and disaster relief, capital flows need signals from governments, government subsidies and tax support. Without the support of such strong policy signals, it would be difficult for us to realize the flow of funds. The theme of this year's World Cities Day is "Financing Sustainable Urban Future for All". Whether in the fields of climate change and disaster relief, or economic development assistance, as well as urban resilience building and infrastructure connectivity in developing countries, a large amount of capital construction requires strong cooperation, which first comes from very clear and strong policy signals. The source of this signal is international trust, which requires both consensus among major powers and cooperation and trust between cities. This kind of trust and cooperation, in fact, provides the most important boost and support for resource flow. At the same time, it can also lead to a positive cycle, forming a policy signal of sustainable development between our government and the world, including capital flow and common development in the fields of economy, society, environment, culture and urban governance. However, in the field of sustainable development this year, we actually face enormous challenges and difficulties.

First of all, according to a report released by the International Monetary Fund (IMF), global economic development in the future, especially that in Europe, will suffer unprecedented shocks and face challenges such as high oil prices, geopolitical conflicts, and challenges in infrastructure and financial investment. In terms of sustainable development, there are unprecedented economic challenges not only in Europe, but also in Africa and other emerging developing countries, including China. In addition, geopolitical conflicts and mistrust among major powers have undermined the foundation of international cooperation on a global scale. The authority of the UN has been challenged and impacted as never before. What will Globalization 2.0 look like? Is it a global win-win situation or a global fragmentation? Will there be a convergence or a split? This will affect the realization of the UN 2030 Sustainable Development Goals, as well as the final realization of the United Nations Framework Convention on Climate Change (UNFCCC), the Paris Agreement and human sustainable development goals.

This year's biggest impact on the Sustainable Development Goals is the intensification of uncertainty, covering the uncertain dynamic foundation for future sustainable development, and various disasters around the world, such as global warming and climate disasters. In particular, disasters caused by climate change have a great impact on us. In this case, the most important thing to eliminate uncertainty is trust, which is based on cooperation at all levels and in all fields. In 2015, when the UN adopted the Paris Agreement and the 2030 Agenda for Sustainable Development, the world's major powers and economies at that time had a very strong willingness to cooperate and trust.

However, after 2017, the rise of populism, anti-globalization and various economic extreme phenomena has had a great impact on the UN Habitat Agenda and the UN 2030 Sustainable Development Goals. In order to understand, implement and promote the inclusive and sustainable development emphasized by the UN 2030 Sustainable Development Goals and the New Urban Agenda and realize more resilient and safer urban cooperation, we need to make greater efforts to promote cooperation among cities, not only from bottom-up but also from top-down.

There are three forms of urban cooperation. One is urban cooperation under the leadership of international organizations, such as the UN, including the World Cities Day held in our country and the "Shanghai Manual". One is cooperation between cities, and the other is cooperation between various actors within a city, such as cooperation between corporate cooperative organizations and multi-stakeholders in the city. This kind of cooperation is constantly upgrading and developing and has achieved various results.

We can see that in the field of intergovernmental cooperation, especially with the expansion of BRICS cooperation mechanism promoted by China, there has been further development in urban cooperation within BRICS countries, including cooperation between China and Central Asian countries and between China and southern African countries. In addition, with the G20 Summit, urban cooperation mechanisms at government level are constantly developing, including the Shanghai Cooperation Organization (SCO) and urban cooperation in the field of the "Belt and Road". For example, China's cooperation with Africa in the field of infrastructure connectivity has played an important role in sustainable urban development.

Besides, multilateral city-to-city cooperation networks have played a variety of roles not only in sustainable development but also in various aspects such as peace, society and human rights, especially in the living welfare of people in developing countries. This kind of global urban cooperation has become an important source to promote and support the sustainable development of the UN. Especially in Africa, global urban cooperation has not only improved the sanitary environment but also greatly enhanced people's quality of life. The cooperation between cities is not only a supplement to the UN development assistance system, but also conducive to knowledge sharing among them. Human knowledge is constantly increasing, and mutual reference of local knowledge is conducive to the development of urban cooperation in all aspects.

In the sustainable development construction and cooperation of various urban platforms, the most important thing is that future cities will cope with more uncertainties in a new, more important, three-dimensional and multi-line urban cooperation mode to realize our community for urban development.

Coordinated Development of Transportation and Cities from a Low-carbon and Inclusive Perspective ——Theory and Practice from Cities in China and Developing Countries

Zhang Chun
Deputy Director and Professor, Department of Urban and Rural Planning, School of Architecture and Arts, Beijing Jiaotong University

This is an excerpt from the author's speech at the International Forum on Green and Low-carbon Building Technologies.

1 Necessity of Multi-sector Synergy for Carbon Emission Reduction

Since September 2020, President Xi Jinping has repeatedly emphasized the goals of carbon peak and carbon neutrality at international conferences. Currently, carbon emissions from global cities account for 70% to 80% of the total, with China's carbon emissions accounting for approximately 27% of the world's total. Cities are the main battleground for carbon neutrality in China. However, there is a lack of key strategy for carbon emission reduction in the urban planning field, and the situation is becoming urgent.

Currently, carbon emissions from transportation and construction sectors collectively account for about one-third of the global total. According to statistics from the China Statistical Yearbook on Environment, carbon emissions from the transportation sector constitute 10.4% of China's total, with urban road transportation accounting for 84% of carbon emissions within the transportation sector. The carbon emission reduction effects of new energy sources are also not yet significant. Therefore, relying solely on reducing carbon emissions in a single sector has very limited effectiveness; it is essential to engage in multi-sector synergy for carbon emission reduction to truly make an impact.

In the 1980s, Peter Calthorpe proposed the New Urbanism planning concept, from which Transit-Oriented Development (TOD) evolved. The TOD concept suggests that its construction of efficient urban structures and intensified land use enhances urban vitality, impacting the urban built environment in a manner that aligns with carbon emission reduction trends:

(1) Compact development to reduce sprawl. TOD's design and development princi-

ples can help cities move away from disorganized urban sprawl, reducing carbon emissions in the process of energy consumption.

(2) Low-carbon travel with the guidance of public transportation. Development oriented toward public transportation encourages the use of public transportation and walking, reducing reliance on cars.

(3) Mixed functions for proximity commuting. Creating mixed-function areas that combine work, commerce, culture, education, and residence helps reduce the separation between work and residence, promoting proximity commuting.

TOD with multi-scale and multi-dimensional transportation focus plays a significant role in carbon emission reduction, especially in forming a comprehensive impact with the combination of "built environment and commuting behavior" in both social and environmental perspectives. From the social perspective, this involves establishing a comprehensive public transportation system based on urban rail transit stations, bus stops, and shared bike parking points; creating high-intensity and diversified transportation corridors along rail transit lines; developing urban spatial structures based on high-density, cluster-based, and diversified development to form short-distance travel demand connections and travel chains around stations; fostering public transportation service guidance and non-essential travel chains for open urban communities along the corridors; achieving work-residence balance for urban residents and reducing long-distance commuting needs in a coordinated effort to reduce carbon emissions (Fig. 1).

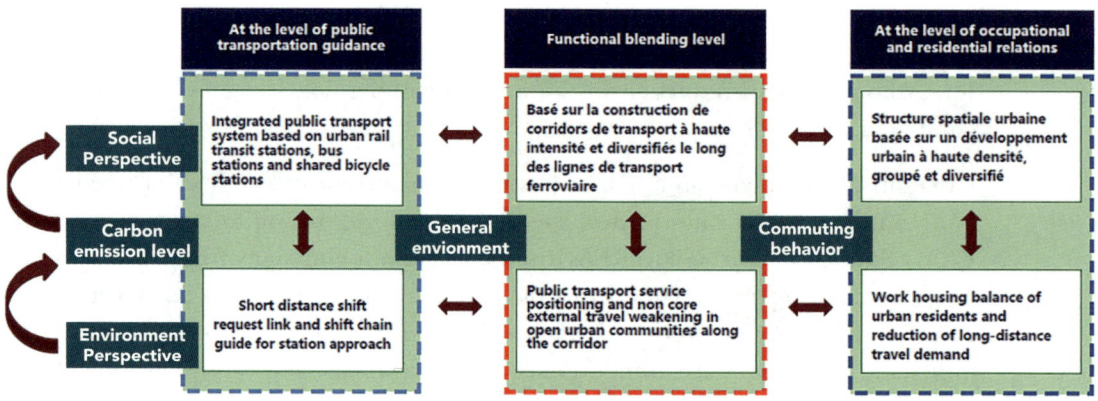

Fig. 1 Multi-scale and multi-dimensional TOD model carbon emission reduction synergy impact diagram (Source: Drawn by the author)

2 TOD Model and Urban Carbon Emission Reduction

The TOD model can bring favorable changes to transportation activities through the optimization of urban structure and guide passengers toward modes of public transportation like rail transit, thereby achieving the goals of ecological balance and energy conservation with emission reduction.

Based on historical data, the TOD model has shown significant environmental benefits for carbon emission reduction in developing countries. According to the simulation analysis in Jakarta, it is projected that with the introduction of TOD, carbon dioxide emissions could decrease by 26%, reaching a level of 350 t, and average fuel consumption could decrease by 20%. In Beijing, compared to population distribution, the improved accessibility following the construction of rail transit further concentrates economic elements, leading to changes in urban employment spaces and resulting in shifts in carbon emission levels. In economically developed regions, as development intensity increases, urban transportation demands become more concentrated, and the integration of a well-developed high-capacity public transportation system enhances the proportion of green travel.

2.1 Compact development to prevent sprawl—Impact of urban form on carbon emissions under TOD model

A study on the impact of urban form on commuting carbon emissions in 279 prefecture-level cities in China revealed several key influencing factors: (1) The expansion of urban built-up areas and the increase in per capita urban road area lead to a higher level of urban commuting carbon emissions. As urban development areas expand and road areas increase, commuting carbon emissions also correspondingly increase. This could be due to the rise in commuting demands and the use of private vehicles. (2) Improving the level of urban public transportation supply is conducive to increasing low-carbon travel choices. Enhancements to the urban public transportation system can encourage residents to opt for public transportation over private vehicles, thereby reducing commuting carbon emissions. This finding underscores the vital role of public transportation in reducing urban carbon emissions. (3) Population density has heterogeneous effects on cities at different stages of development. Generally, cities with higher population densities may find it easier to implement efficient public transportation systems and urban planning, thereby reducing carbon emissions.

In conclusion, for a large city like Beijing, there should be a focus on controlling the expansion of built-up areas to minimize unnecessary urban sprawl and reduce the stimulation of carbon emissions, increasing investment in and improving the public transportation system, enhancing service levels, and encouraging more residents to choose low-carbon travel options. Considering Beijing's status as a high-density city, further optimization of urban planning and transportation management can enhance efficiency and reduce carbon emissions.

2.2 Mixed functions for proximity commuting—Analysis of carbon emissions from work-residence space in Beijing under TOD model

From the distribution and changes in population density in Beijing, the city is showing a trend of transitioning from central agglomeration toward radial expansion. The increasing connection between population concentration areas and transportation infrastructure is becoming more apparent, especially in the suburban areas and on the outskirts of employment centers. Between 2000 and 2010, Beijing's employment positions showed a trend of centralizing toward the city center, forming a pattern of a single employment center with the central urban area as its core. However, from 2010 to 2020, despite the expansion of the employment center space in the city center, there was a strengthening trend toward partial concentration. Simultaneously, industrial parks and administrative centers in the suburbs also gradually developed into distinct secondary employment centers, prompting the development of a multi-center employment pattern in the city.

In 2020, the permanent resident population in the central urban area of Beijing was about 10.99 million, accounting for 50.2% of the total population. Compared to 2010, the permanent resident population decreased by 728,000, a decrease of 9.5%. Despite changes in population spatial characteristics, the phenomenon of separation between work and residence has not been effectively alleviated. Employment positions continue to centralize toward the center, while residents are shifting toward the outskirts of the city, exacerbating the imbalance of work and residence, with the city center being dominated by employment and the outer suburbs being dominated by residential purposes.

Under the influence of the TOD model, the supply level of public transportation facilities significantly impacts the per capita carbon emissions. In areas with high bus coverage, the per capita commuting carbon emissions are 691 g, significantly lower than the 1,499 g in areas with low bus coverage, where the carbon emissions are 2.17 times higher than those in the former. In residential communities with good accessibility to rail transit, the per capita commuting carbon emissions are 977 g, while in areas with poor accessibility, they are 1,283 g, with the latter emitting 1.3 times more carbon than the former. In residential communities with high bus coverage, the per kilometer per capita carbon emissions are 44.1 g, whereas in areas with low coverage, they are 65.9 g. In residential communities with good accessibility to rail transit, the per kilometer per capita carbon emissions are 50.1 g, compared to 68.3 g in areas with poor accessibility.

From the perspective of changes in the relationship between work and residence spaces, income level is a significant factor influencing commuting behavior. Studies indicate that as income increases, commuting distances show a slow upward trend, particularly when incomes reach the range of RMB 8,000 to RMB 10,000 and exceed RMB 15,000, where commuting distances peak significantly. After the income surpasses RMB 12,000, commuting carbon emissions notably increase, possibly due to residents being more inclined to choose to commute by car.

The research team selected the Dashilar and Caochang communities on both sides of Qianmen Street, as well as the Tiantongyuan Residential Community on the outskirts of the central urban area in Beijing for in-depth study. Qualitative interviews revealed that Dashilar and Caochang communities are closer to the city center, providing relatively shorter commuting distances for residents. These areas have higher employment densities, offering residents more flexibility in choosing their places of work. Factors influencing conventional bus commuting include distance to bus stops, walkability, and ease of transfers. Commuters show a preference for bus stops that are closer in distance (Fig. 2).

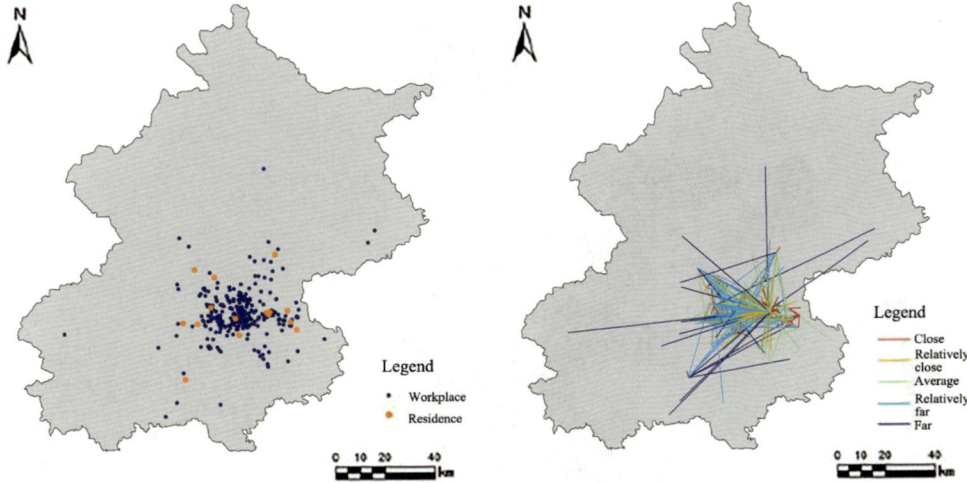

Fig. 2 Distribution of places of residence and work of Beijing residents' commuting sample
(Source: *Impact of Urban Built Environment on Commuting Carbon Emissions—Taking Beijing as an Example*, Zhang Chun, Ning Yanhao, and Liang Ying, Shanghai Urban Planning Review, 2023)

These findings highlight that under the TOD model, by implementing the strategy of mixed functions and proximity commuting, it is possible to effectively reduce urban residents' commuting carbon emissions while enhancing their quality of life and employment opportunities.

2.3 Low-carbon travel with the guidance of public transportation—Impact of TOD on the travel of all groups from an inclusive perspective

In the process of building a TOD that satisfies the people, it is not just a slogan but also a policy action. Taking Urumqi as an example, the city has already constructed seven BRT routes, with plans for three metro lines to cover the entire city. The average daily number of trips per resident in Urumqi is 2.47 times per person per day. In terms of time consumption, the shortest commuting time for non-motorized vehicles is 22 mins, while the longest time for motorized vehicles is 42.3 mins. Regarding commuting modes, walking has the highest percentage, while taxi usage is the lowest.

After the introduction of the TOD concept, the work-to-residence ratio based on TAZ (Traffic Analysis Zone) along the BRT lines increased from 2010 to 2014, indicating that the BRT has brought more job opportunities to those constrained by time and travel costs. However, it is important to note that the impact of the BRT on remote suburban areas is relatively limited (Fig. 3).

3 Necessity of Low-carbon Development in Developing Countries

In Phnom Penh, Cambodia, private motorcycles and tuk-tuks typically use fuel as a power source, leading to significant emissions of greenhouse gases and pollutants that severely pollute the environment. To reduce these emissions and improve air quality, the government of Phnom Penh plans to promote a public transportation system.

Chapter I Future Cities and Sustainable Development

Fig. 3 Schematic diagram of work-to-residence ratio along Urumqi BRT lines from 2010 to 2014
(Source: *Study on the Impact of Public Transportation Infrastructure on the Employment of Low-income Groups in Urumqi*, Zhang Chun, Cheng Zhihua, Yu Xiaoping, Wang Yaqun, and Shen Chen, Progress in Geography, 2020)

Particularly against the backdrop of urban modernization and increasing travel needs of residents, Phnom Penh aims to address longstanding transportation constraints and enhance employment accessibility for middle- and low-income residents by implementing TOD strategy.

However, despite the conventional bus routes under the TOD strategy helping to improve accessibility between newly developed suburban communities and the city center in Phnom Penh, they face challenges in covering the most impoverished low-income communities in the city. Results from a small-sample survey on public transportation usage and satisfaction indicate that opting for public transportation can significantly reduce commuting times for low-income groups and those who need to commute long distances. However, there are still many low-income and long-distance commuting groups that have not fully benefited from these services.

Therefore, for a city in developing country like Phnom Penh, low-carbon development is crucial. By enhancing the public transportation system, especially through strategically expanding coverage to include low-income communities, it is possible to not only reduce the use of private petrol-powered vehicles and lower carbon emissions but also improve air quality and enhance residents' quality of life and employment opportunities. This initiative not only contributes to environmental sustainability but also aligns with the urgent global need to reduce carbon emissions and address climate change.

The Government, Enterprises, and the Public Cooperate to Promote the Sustainable Development of Bus Services

Cheng Shidong
Director, Center of Urban Transport, Institute of Comprehensive Transportation, National Development and Reform Commission

This is an excerpt from the author's speech at the special forum themed "Sustainable Transport and the Future of Cities".

1 Logic of Urban Buses

Buses first appeared in London, England. In the beginning, it operated entirely on a market basis, with the public directly purchasing transportation services from bus companies. With continuous development, nowadays, most countries and cities view buses as having strong public welfare characteristics and consider them a fundamental public service. Thus, in the entire process and elements, in addition to the public and businesses, the government (Fig. 1) appears. The government leads in determining route settings, frequency of service, fares, and discounts, and bears the policy-related losses incurred in the process.

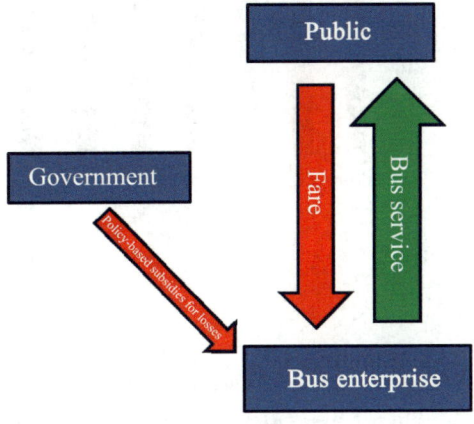

Fig. 1 Public transportation participants and their relationships

2 Reasons for Current Operating Difficulties

Currently, the financial sustainability situation of buses is extremely severe. What are the reasons leading to this? I think there are three main aspects.

Firstly, the costs are rising. The service standards set by the government, such as route settings, frequency of services, target groups for discounts, and their extent, have remained largely unchanged over the years. However, costs, including vehicle purchases, staff salaries, fuel prices, and vehicle maintenance expenses, have significantly increased.

Secondly, the decline in revenue is more significant. Bus revenue is related to two factors: Ticket prices and passenger volume. In terms of ticket prices, the vast majority of cities nationwide have maintained relatively low levels over the past 10 to 20 years, reflecting considerations for people's well-being and public welfare. Ticket prices have not increased, but passenger volumes have significantly decreased. From a national perspective, the passenger volume of conventional buses has been continuously declining since 2014, over nearly 10 years. The COVID-19 pandemic has exacerbated this downward trend (the pandemic only accelerated the decline; even without the pandemic, the decline would have continued gradually) (Fig. 2). In 2022, the passenger volume decreased to 45.2% of the peak point in 2014.

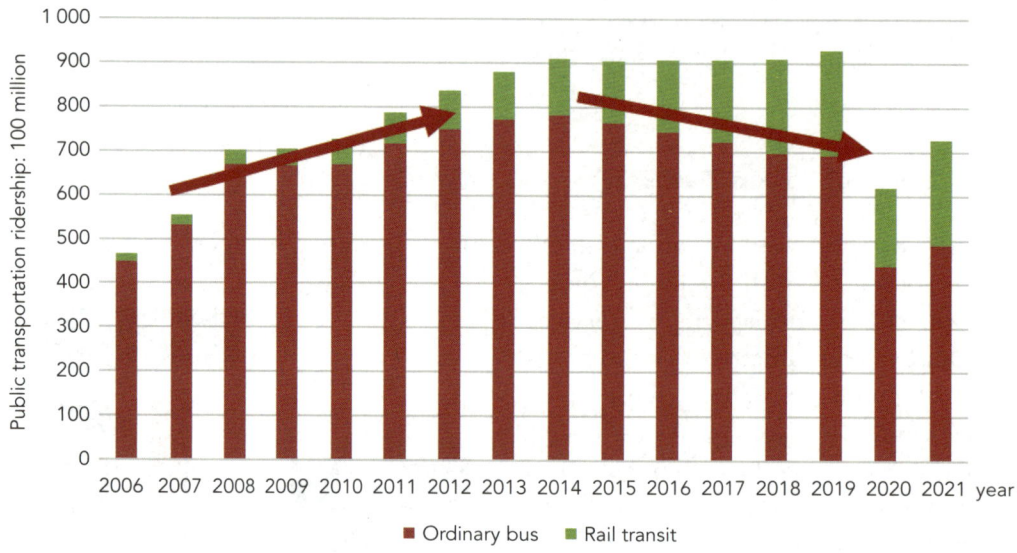

Fig. 2 Changes in public transportation ridership in recent years

As the aging population continues to grow, the number and percentage of individuals eligible for free rides on conventional buses have increased rapidly. In most cities, this percentage has exceeded 40%, while some smaller cities in West China have reached as high as 80%. The total passenger volume is decreasing, with the proportion of free riders increasing, leading to a sharp decline in revenue from bus fares.

The rapid decline in passenger volume of buses, especially for conventional buses, can be attributed to the following two reasons.

Firstly, the appeal and competitiveness of over-ground public transportation have not significantly increased. Since the 18th National Congress of the Communist Party of China, both at the national and local levels, significant efforts have been made in the field of buses, resulting in noticeable achievements such as a significant increase in dedicated bus lanes and the utilization rate of buses. However, in terms of convenience and speed for the public, the competitiveness and attractiveness have not improved significantly.

Secondly, external environmental changes have had a greater impact. For the one part, the rapid expansion of rail transit networks has attracted and diverted some passenger flows. In addition to rail transit, the rapid increase in the ownership of private cars by households has had a significant impact. Moreover, the more substantial influence comes from the rapid growth of electric bicycles. In the past 20 years, electric bicycles have grown at a faster rate compared to private cars, and currently, the total number of electric bicycles in use exceeds that of private cars in use (Fig. 3).

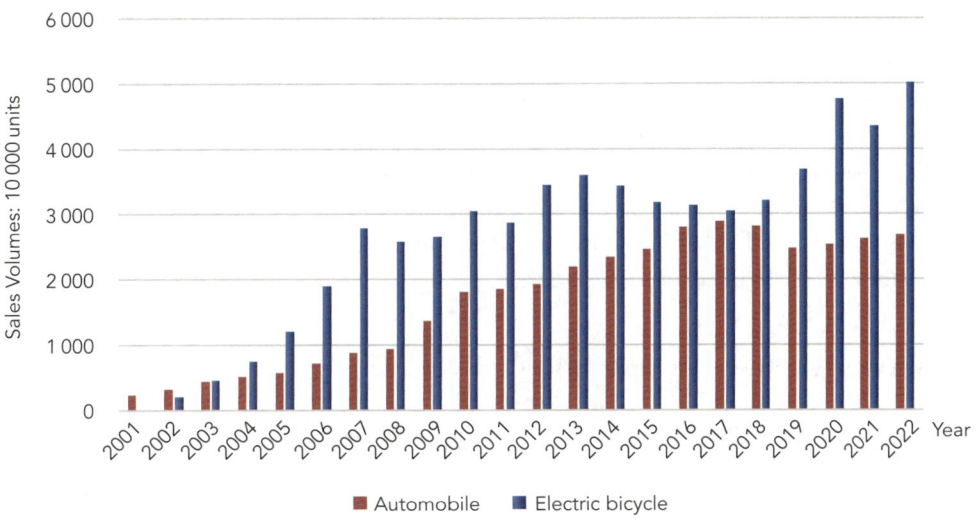

Fig. 3 Sales volumes of automobiles and electric bicycles in recent years

Electric bicycles not only have a high usage rate but are also used frequently. A research report (similar to my survey) shows that in first-tier cities, the usage frequency of electric bicycles, cars, and buses is roughly equal. In second-tier cities, the usage frequency of electric bicycles is 1.5 times that of cars and buses. In small and medium-sized cities, the usage frequency of electric bicycles is 2.5 times that of buses and three times that of private cars (Tab. 1).

Tab. 1　Usage rates of means of transportation in different types of cities

City type	Private car	Bus	Electric bicycle	By foot
First-tier cities	21.8%	29.4%	24.6%	24.2%
Second-tier cities	20.7%	22.4%	30.1%	26.8%
Small and medium-sized cities	14.6%	15.5%	37.5%	32.4%

Personally, I believe that the main reason for the decrease in the passenger volume of conventional buses is the attractiveness of rail transit, cars, and electric bicycles. The lack of its own attractiveness and competitiveness is a secondary reason, with the ratio of the two influences being 3:7. When it comes to the development of urban transportation in China, it is essential to address the issues related to electric bicycles, rather than turn a blind eye to them. We must contemplate the possible status of electric bicycles in the next 10 to 20 years, as well as proper management and guidance strategies.

Thirdly, speaking of reasons for the operational difficulties faced by buses, apart from increased costs and significant revenue decrease, another factor is the reduction in government subsidies. Before 2019, the central government provided relatively substantial subsidies for oil and new energy vehicles. After a significant reduction in subsidies by the central government in 2019, local and city governments did not fully implement their related responsibilities. City governments such as Beijing, Shanghai, Guangzhou, and Shenzhen provide substantial and effective subsidies for buses. However, from a national perspective, the majority of city governments do not offer much substantial subsidy support. With reduced national subsidies, bus companies can benefit from few government subsidies. With rising costs, significant decreases in ticket revenues, and subsidies failing to keep pace, the financial sustainability of bus companies becomes difficult to maintain.

3 Ways to Achieve Sustainability

The future sustainable development of buses should revolve around the following aspects.

Firstly, reducing costs. The government should adjust city public transportation service standards appropriately. Buses should be included in the category of national basic public services, with each city determining its own standards based on its financial capabilities. Service standards should be considered from the perspective of passenger flow volume while also aligning with financial capabilities. Currently, passenger flow volume is less than half of that in 2014, with a significant decrease in passenger numbers. In this context, it may be appropriate to slightly reduce the frequency of bus departures. Indeed, it is essential to maintain a specific frequency to ensure the service level and quality are consistently upheld. The downsizing of vehicle models can adapt to the decrease in passenger flow and, to a certain extent, ensure the frequency of departures. In theory, the downsizing of vehicle models, personnel costs, and management are primarily the responsibility of the bus enterprises, while the government can set requirements and provide guidance.

Secondly, increasing ticket revenue. We often say that ticket prices should be "acceptable by residents, affordable by the government, and sustainable for businesses". Among these, it is essential to ensure the sustainability of businesses. As a business, financial sustainability is crucial, with a balance between revenue and expenses and a certain level of profitability. How can the public and government balance their interests when business sustainability remains unchanged? It is often difficult to accommodate both sides. For the public, lower ticket prices are preferred, but can the government afford it? In most cities in our country, bus fares have not changed in nearly 20 years; however, there should be a certain degree of increase in ticket revenue.

Will raising ticket prices cause people to stop using buses? Whether or not people choose to use buses depends on various factors, including ticket prices, but the key drivers are speed, timing, and reliability. In big cities, subway ticket prices are higher than buses, yet many people choose to ride the subway because it is faster and more reliable. To enhance the attractiveness and competitiveness of conventional buses, the focus should be put on speed, reliability, and convenience, including necessary bus lanes, more convenient connections at both ends, and others. In the future, it is imperative to explore ways to consistently elevate the appeal and competitiveness of buses while ensuring financial sustainability.

Thirdly, bus companies should fully leverage their resources to increase revenue. The most significant revenue source that bus companies can capitalize is their land properties. The comprehensive development of land may be constrained by land policies and could take a considerable amount of time to yield results. Furthermore, the current state of the real estate market also impacts the value of land development, which may not be as lucrative as before. Other options include customized bus services, advertising, gas stations, natural gas stations, maintenance services, and so on. Customized bus services, such as commuter shuttles for business, should be market-driven. Conventional buses serve as a fundamental public service and are welfare-oriented. However, within public transportation, there are elements of complete marketization, such as customized bus services, which combine both welfare and market-driven aspects.

Fourthly, government subsidies must be sufficient and timely. The government-set service standards, including discount levels and beneficiary groups, must be fully implemented with full-amount subsidies. It cannot be that the government promises free services for people aged 60 and above, with businesses footing the bill.

After the government has set service standards and subsidy levels, determining the policy-induced losses becomes a challenging issue. A mature approach is cost planning, exemplified by Shenzhen, which has been exploring this for many years. Cost planning is currently an effective method, but it also has its shortcomings. It is challenging to stimulate and improve a company's management efficiency, such as determining the number of employees, work efficiency, and organizational efficiency. It is necessary to explore and experiment with a service purchasing model under specific competitive conditions. The United States' National Aeronautics and Space Administration (NASA) used to launch satellites under cost planning, resulting in high costs and long development cycles. Elon Musk proposed to NASA the idea of paying based on the final service result: Paying for the payload weight sent into space. This approach resembles a competitive or market mechanism. This is an effective way to reduce government subsidies or better understand the extent of subsidies provided. This requires the involvement of different market entities, especially private ones. Having a transparent government subsidy and evaluation system is crucial. Many governments are hesitant to provide subsidies for private enterprises because of the lack of openness and transparency in the system. If subsidies are given to private enterprises, concerns arise regarding potential issues such as profit transfer and loss of state-owned assets. Therefore, it is crucial to establish a transparent subsidy and evaluation system.

4 Call for Increasing of Central Government Support

Public transportation exhibits strong regional characteristics, with the municipal people's governments bearing primary responsibility while the central government should also have a certain level of responsibility. Regarding essential public services such as education and healthcare, from the perspective of equalizing public services, the central government holds a certain level of responsibility. This is reflected in reality, with the central government making expenditures on these basic public services. Public transportation is a green and low-carbon mode of travel, representing an important decarbonization measure in the transportation sector. It has contributed to achieving dual carbon goals, extending beyond the scope of localities and regional cities to a national and even global level. The central government thus should provide a certain level of financial support for this cause.

From a practical standpoint, whether in the United States, Europe, or other countries and regions, the central governments have subsidized urban public transportation, including its construction and operation. The practices in our country have also demonstrated that support from the central government level is highly effective. Before 2019, the total amount of subsidies from the central government for oil and new energy vehicles was not particularly large, totaling around RMB 30 to 40 billion. A significant portion of small and medium-sized cities relied on these national subsidies (without subsidies at the city level) to sustain the operation of buses, demonstrating the important role played by national subsidies. Compared to trillions of yuan invested in transportation infrastructure nationwide each year, if we shift the development focus of transportation from infrastructure construction to transport services and allocate an additional two to three percentage points, we can effectively ensure the financial sustainability of buses. The division of responsibilities between the central government and local governments is a significant topic closely related to the financial and tax systems (Fig. 4).

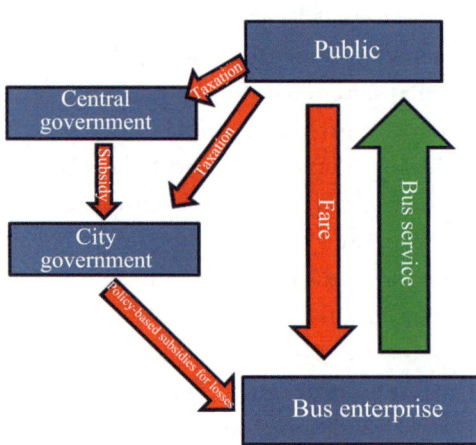

Fig. 4 Relationships of central and local governments at all levels with enterprises and the public

From a practical perspective, local governments are currently facing tight financial constraints. The central government must allocate certain funds to support urban bus services. The central government should research and consider establishing stable channels for financial support, along with clear and transparent mechanisms for distribution and assessment.

Accelerating Urban "Carbon Neutrality": Domestic and International Practices

Xue Lulu
Director of WRI (United States) China Sustainable Transition Center, Beijing Office

> This is an excerpt from the author's speech at the 2023 World Cities Day "Urban Environment" Theme Forum and the 4th Shanghai International Urban Furniture Summit Forum.

Cities are crucial carriers of population and economic life, and they are also the major contributors to carbon emissions. According to statistical data, cities account for over 80% of Chinese energy-related carbon emissions. In the future, with the increase in population and the further advancement of urbanization, cities will be the main battlefield for achieving the "Dual Carbon" goals.

In fact, cities are also expected to take the lead in Chinese "Dual Carbon" goals. As early as 2010, the National Development and Reform Commission (NDRC) announced a low-carbon city pilot project, proposing that 81 pilot cities should achieve peak carbon emissions by 2030, which is earlier than the time when China put forward the "Dual Carbon" Goals.

According to the analysis of WRI (World Resources Institute) model, Chinese cities are very likely to achieve "carbon neutrality" by 2050. With the current technological level, such as renewable energy technology for electricity and new energy vehicle technologies, Chinese cities are expected to achieve a 50% deep reduction in carbon emissions by 2050. Given that technology is no longer the main obstacle for cities to achieve deep emission reduction in the medium and long term, the key question is how to ensure the policies enable cities to achieve their medium and long-term emission reduction goals. To answer this question, WRI spent one year developing the Citysphere Data Platform, which aggregates low-carbon development goals and policies from over 1,000 cities worldwide. We also quantitatively analyzed the current level of urban low-carbon development, hoping that this platform can offer references in formulating climate goals and actions for decision-makers.

Firstly, in terms of setting low-carbon goals, we systematically reviewed whether more than 1,000 cities around the world have set "carbon neutrality" goals and timetables. Overall, 209 cities around the world have issued their "Carbon Neutrality" goals, mainly in developed countries with over 70% of them having set such goals. However, it is worth noting that "carbon neutrality" goals are not exclusive to developed countries. According to statistics, 84 cities in developing countries have set "Carbon Neutrality" goals, accounting for half of the global cities with such goals, including São Paulo in Brazil, Mexico City in Mexico and African cities such as Lagos in Nigeria.

Regarding the time for achieving urban "carbon neutrality" goals, most global cities aim for 2050, though some developed countries, especially in Europe, have set their goals earlier than 2050. Over 1/3 of European cities aim to achieve "carbon neutrality" goals earlier than 2040 (Fig. 1).

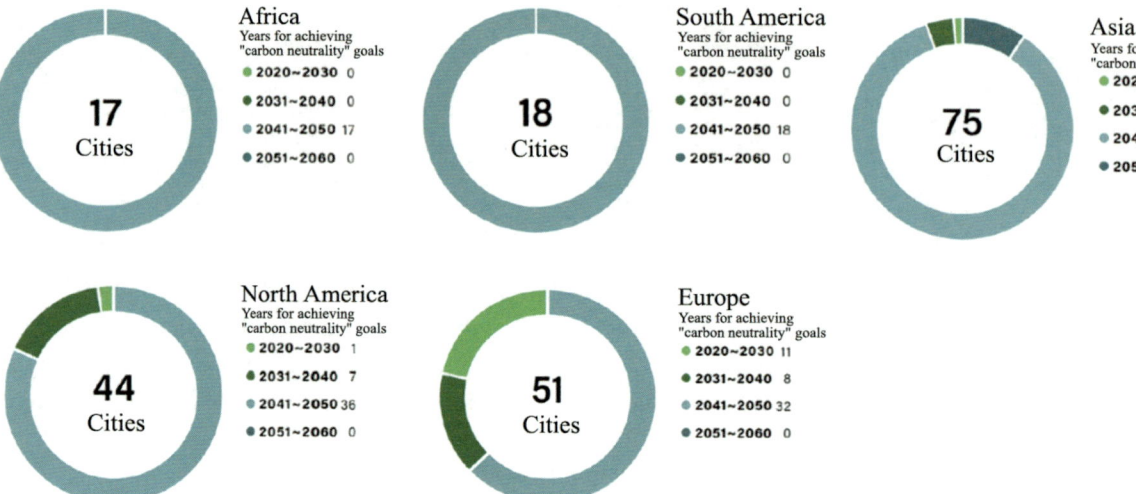

Fig. 1 Time for achieving urban "carbon neutrality" goals

By comparing the time for achieving urban "carbon neutrality" with that of the country, from a global perspective, it can be seen that the two are consistent, which is a top-down and tiered decomposition model. The only exception is European cities, where urban goals are 10 ~ 20 years ahead of that of the country.

In addition to setting the "carbon neutrality" goals, we quantitatively analyzed the current situation of low-carbon development in cities, especially the differences between domestic and foreign cities, and identified aspects where we need to improve.

First of all, it is necessary to ensure that cities are comparable. There are more than 600 cities in China with vast differences in size and economic development stages. From an emissions perspective, there are production-oriented cities in China like Tangshan and Ningbo, where industrial and power sectors dominate the industrial, economic and carbon emission structure. In addition, there are consumption-oriented cities like Beijing, Shanghai, Guangzhou, and Shenzhen, whose industrial structure is mainly service-oriented and carbon emissions from transportation and buildings prevail. The significant differences between these city types mean that their low-carbon development paths also vary greatly.

We categorized cities into industrial, agricultural, and service-oriented types according to the industrial structures. And we analyzed them across four dimensions: low-carbon production, low-carbon consumption, low-carbon environment, and low-carbon progress. According to different indicators and weights, we calculated an overall score for each city's low-carbon development. The results show that service-oriented cities generally perform better in low-carbon development than industrial and agricultural cities at home and abroad, highlighting the importance of economic and industrial structure upgrading for achieving low-carbon development.

Even within service-oriented and industrial cities, there are variations. For example, in China's service-oriented cities, the low-carbon development performance of megacities is better than that of second and third-tier cities. Among the industrial cities, coastal developed areas like Foshan and Dongguan outperform others. Every city is unique, so the low-carbon development strategies need to be tailored to local conditions.

Comparing the overall low-carbon development scores of Chinese cities with international cities systematically, Chinese cities have a competitive edge globally but still have room for improvement in low-carbon production (reductions in power and industrial emissions) and low-carbon environment (forest coverage and air pollution control).

With the "carbon neutrality" goals and the current development situation, cities need to formulate corresponding low-carbon policies. Our systematic review of 12 global cities shows an increasing emphasis on low-carbon development policies, with nearly 100 policies introduced over the past decade covering all aspects of many key areas, 60% of which were issued after 2017, indicating a growing global focus on low-carbon development.

Analyzing the industry coverage of these low-carbon policies, they mainly focus on three aspects: waste management, energy and water utilities, and local government operations. The relatively weak areas are city-level initiatives, building policies, transportation policies and green finance. Cities with relatively low industry coverage in their low-carbon development policies include the previously mentioned European cities. This implies that in addition to having ambitious "carbon neutrality" goals, these cities must implement more aggressive policies to ensure these goals are achieved (Tab. 1).

London ranks first among the 12 cities, characterized by wide-ranging and robust low-carbon policies, particularly in the transportation and building sectors. For example, London proposed to set up zero-emission zones in its urban central areas by 2025, restricting fuel-powered cars and promoting new energy vehicles, which has a great impact on the promotion of new energy vehicle policies. In addition, London proposed city-wide heating system emissions reductions by 2030, achieving zero emissions in transportation and buildings by 2050. This policy was formulated by multiple government departments with high coordination and consistency. This means that cross-sectoral communication and coordination is very important if cities are to achieve low-carbon development (Fig. 2).

Tab. 1 Assessment results of climate policy coverage in 12 cities

City	City-level initiatives	Building policy	Transport policy	Green finance	Waste management	Energy and water utilities	Local government operations
London	Relatively high	High	High	Medium	High	High	High
Shanghai	High	Relatively high	Relatively high	High	High	High	High
Shenzhen	High	Relatively high	Relatively high	High	High	High	High
Singapore	Relatively high	Relatively high	Relatively high	High	High	High	High
New York	Medium	Relatively high	Relatively high	High	High	High	High
Los Angeles	Relatively high	Relatively high	Relatively high	Medium	High	Relatively high	High
Copenhagen	High	Medium	High	Medium	High	Medium	High
Johannesburg	Relatively high	High	Medium	High	Relatively high	Medium	Medium
Guilin	Medium	Relatively high	Medium	Relatively high	Relatively high	Relatively high	High
São Paulo	Relatively high	Relatively low	Relatively high	Relatively high	High	Relatively high	Medium
Melbourne	Medium	Medium	Medium	Medium	Medium	Relatively high	High
Mexico city	Relatively high	Relatively low	Medium	High	Relatively high	Medium	High

To achieve low-carbon development, cities must accelerate the construction and improvement of data systems, set climate reduction goals tailored to local conditions, scientifically formulate low-carbon roadmaps and action plans, and ensure the implementation of these plans through diverse measures. WRI has been long committed to building a global urban low-carbon development information platform and partnering with Chinese cities, leveraging our research strengths and data to support urban low-carbon and sustainable development in China.

Fig. 2 London's "carbon neutrality" roadmaps

Chapter I Future Cities and Sustainable Development

Giving Full Play to the Crucial Role of the Carbon Market and Uniting Diverse Forces to Propel Urban Green Transformation

Liu Jie
General Manager of Shanghai Environment and Energy Exchange

> This is an excerpt from the author's speech at the "Green Development and Financing for Sustainable Development Forum".

"World Cities Day" is the first city-themed international day established by the United Nations and also the first international day initiated by the Chinese government. The theme of this year's China Observance is "Financing Sustainable Urban Future for All", which provides an open and shared exchange platform for promoting global cities to build a better and sustainable life. It is a great honor to be invited to attend this forum and discuss with experts from core fields such as finance, environment, and science and technology how the emission reduction mechanism can give full play to its supporting role in the process of urban green transformation.

Cities are the center and main space carrier of human economic and social activities, as well as the main source of greenhouse gas emissions. According to relevant survey data, 70% of China's carbon emissions come from urban activities. It is expected that this proportion will rise to 80% by 2030. Therefore, promoting energy conservation and emission reduction in cities and green carbon reduction for all people and gradually forming a green and low-carbon production and lifestyle are of great significance to advance China's carbon emission reduction and promote the realization of goals of carbon peak and carbon neutrality.

On September 22, 2020, China announced its commitment to carbon peak in 30 years and carbon neutrality in 60 years at the 75th General Debate of the United Nations General Assembly for the first time. With this as its goal, it issued the Opinions on Implementing the New Development Philosophy in Full, Accurate and All-round Ways to Achieve Carbon Peak and Carbon Neutrality and the Action Plan for Carbon Peak Before 2030. As programmatic documents for the "dual carbon" goals, they guide all provinces, industries and enterprises to formulate action plans for carbon peak and carbon neutrality based on their actual development. The "1+N" dual carbon policy system has been initially formed. In July 2022, Shanghai issued the Implementation Plan for Carbon Peak in Shanghai (hereinafter referred to as the "Plan") to actively implement national policies and make solid progress in carbon peak. The

Plan details key tasks in 10 aspects, including "green and low-carbon energy transformation", "energy conservation, carbon reduction and efficiency improvement", "urban and rural construction" and "transportation construction", to systematically promote the city's work of carbon peak. In terms of "energy conservation, carbon reduction and efficiency improvement" "green transportation" "circular economy" and "green and low-carbon action for all", the Plan proposes to comprehensively improve energy utilization efficiency and benefits in the whole society, actively guide citizens' green and low-carbon travel, establish a circular society, and comprehensively consolidate the effectiveness of domestic waste classification. In addition, the Plan proposes to build a national waste classification demonstration city, enhance the the public awareness of saving, low carbon and environmental protection, vigorously advocate simple and moderate consumption concepts, comprehensively promote a civilized and healthy lifestyle, and form a good atmosphere for the whole society to consciously practice a green and low-carbon lifestyle. These actions aim to build a multi-subject, wide-area and multi-interactive regional environmental governance system based on urban production and life.

1 Promoting the Coordinated Governance of Regional Environment through Mechanism Construction, Innovation and Guarantee

First, we shall establish a long-term mechanism to improve the efficiency of resource allocation. Specifically, we shall strengthen the construction of market-oriented mechanisms such as those for carbon market trading and pollution rights trading, optimize incentive and restraint mechanisms, effectively manage environmental factors and indicators, improve resource allocation efficiency, integrate resources from all parties to increase investment, and stimulate endogenous social power.

Second, special attention should be paid to market-oriented mechanism innovation with cross-field and comprehensive synergistic benefits. For example, we shall explore the construction of the carbon inclusion mechanism, focus on circular economy development, resource recycling and utilization and garbage classification and disposal, and promote the construction of green waste-free cities. Efforts shall be made to actively develop forest, grass and farmland carbon sinks, consolidate and improve the carbon sink capacity of ecosystems, and strive to build a beautiful and ecological village. We shall pay attention to the transformation of public lifestyles such as energy-saving renovation, green travel and paperless consumption and office, further promote the construction of an energy-saving low-carbon city, encourage the public to actively participate in implementation activities for carbon neutrality, and gradually enhance the awareness of social responsibility for low-carbon environmental protection throughout society. Efforts shall also be made to innovate diversified carbon financial services based on the development path of green finance, guide social capital to flow into green and low-carbon projects or activities, and strengthen support for the whole chain regional environmental management service system.

Third, we shall break through the bottleneck of mechanism development and unleash innovation momentum. Efforts should be made to clarify the institutional barriers that restrict regional environmental governance and high-quality economic and social development, strive to remove obstacles to development based on reality, continuously enhance the leading capacity of regional coordination and innovation, solidly promote mechanism reform and innovation, improve cross-departmental linkage and cooperation and resource allocation efficiency, fully release the synergy effect, and promote urban green and low-carbon transformation.

2 Promoting Carbon Reduction for All by Establishing a Carbon Inclusion Mechanism and Building a Multilevel Carbon Market System

China attaches great importance to the construction of ecological civilization, actively advocates a green and low-carbon lifestyle, and encourages the establishment of an environmental governance system with "multi-participation and benign interaction". At present, all regions are actively exploring low-carbon equity innovation and the establishment of a "carbon inclusion" emission reduction mechanism.

The carbon inclusion mechanism is an incentive mechanism for all people to reduce emissions and an innovative model to realize ecological value. During the design and operation, the carbon inclusion mechanism emphasizes both environmental benefits and inclusiveness. By incorporating small and medium-sized emission reduction projects and public scenarios, combined with transaction realization, policy support, commercial incentives and other means, it guides the public to actively participate in emission reduction, bringing together multiple forces to create a green and low-carbon social atmosphere.

As an important part of the multilevel carbon market, the carbon inclusion mechanism focuses on emission reduction fields close to public life such as basic necessities of life and integrates "small-scale, miscellaneous and decentralized" emission reduction behaviors, such as development and utilization of distributed renewable energy, recycling of resources, green and low-carbon travel, agricultural emission reduction or carbon sink. It has expanded the scope of national and local carbon emission management in the process of urban development and gradually explored all-round, multi-field and deep-seated green emission reduction. At the same time, some regions have guided carbon inclusion emission reductions into local carbon emissions trading markets through quota performance offset mechanisms, providing a strong supplement to the mandatory quota market and further activating the vitality of the carbon market.

At present, China's carbon inclusion mechanism focuses on regional independent exploration in top-level design, management and operation. The development of the carbon inclusion mechanism presents a trend of "combining points and aspects", with 11 provinces, 23 municipalities/districts, 1 autonomous region and 3 counties/parks now actively building and implementing the carbon inclusion mechanism. For example, Shanghai carried out research on the carbon inclusion mechanism as early as 2019. In November 2022, 8 departments including the Shanghai Municipal Bureau of Ecology and Environment jointly issued the Work Plan for the Construction of Shanghai's Carbon Inclusion System (hereinafter referred to as the "Work Plan"), proposing to actively explore the establishment of regional personal carbon accounts and create a carbon inclusion mechanism model in Shanghai. Based on the Work Plan, Shanghai drafted the Measures on Carbon Inclusion Management in Shanghai and supporting implementation rules, which were officially released in September 2023 to provide guidance and technical support for the operation and development of Shanghai's carbon inclusion system.

With the expansion and deepening of the carbon inclusion mechanism construction, there is still room for exploration and optimization in strengthening incentives and improving the sustainable operation capacity of the carbon inclusion mechanism. First, the incentive methods of the carbon inclusion mechanism will be more diversified, and we will continuously enrich incentive methods and products to further mobilize the public's enthusiasm for emission reduction. For example, we will support the realization of emission reduction trading and voluntary carbon offset, provide honor incentives, enrich convertible equity goods or services, strengthen innovation in carbon financial derivative products, and improve the value of carbon assets. Second, the publicity of the carbon inclusion mechanism needs to be strengthened, and there is still room for improvement in the awareness and acceptance of the carbon inclusion mechanism by all sectors of society. By optimizing publicity and promotion strategies, integrating online digital media and offline citizen interaction activities and other communication channels, we will enhance the public's understanding of and attention to the carbon inclusion mechanism. Third, the cost-effectiveness of enterprise participation needs to be improved, and the income from carbon assets is unstable, making it difficult to cover the participation costs in a short time. By promoting carbon financial innovation and encouraging institutions to set up the carbon inclusion funds, we will provide carbon financial services for participants of the carbon inclusion mechanism, guide social capital flow to emission reduction activities, and enhance financial support. Finally, the level of policy guidance and digital management needs to be improved. Due to the lack of higher-level laws and unified policy guidelines, the construction and promotion efficiency of the carbon inclusion mechanism in various regions has been affected. At the same time, the level of digitization and informatization is also one of the key factors affecting the smooth operation and effective management of the carbon inclusion mechanism. By continuously improving the design of mechanism standards, we will provide support for guiding and regulating market participation behaviors and make the mechanism more scientific, rigorous and reasonable. At the same time, by introducing blockchain technology, we will improve the informatization, digitization, intelligence and safety management of the carbon inclusion mechanism to ensure the smooth, orderly, safe and effective operation of the mechanism.

3 Emphasizing the "Bottom-Up" New Model of Multilevel Global Climate Governance in the Mandatory Emission Reduction Market

The early Paris Agreement emphasized a "bottom-up" new model of multilevel global climate governance. Countries and regions participate in independent emission reduction and plan high-quality development goals and tasks, which has gradually become one of the hot spots of current climate change mitigation issues.

Through mandatory carbon quota fulfillment requirements, combined with the market supply and demand mechanism, we have optimized resource allocation, promoted industrial structure adjustment and green and low-carbon technological innovation, and forced urban key emission units to promote emission reduction. At the same time, we have released effective price signals to guide the flow of factor resources to green emission reduction activities and support enterprises' green and low-carbon transformation.

China started the pilot construction of the carbon market in 2013. Up to now, there are 9 pilot local carbon markets. After more than 10 years of development, the national carbon market and regional pilot markets have developed synchronously. China has steadily promoted the development of the mandatory carbon market and actively participated in international voluntary emission reduction mechanism. In order to further expand the field and scope of greenhouse gas emission reduction and build a multilevel carbon market system, China has gradually explored the construction of the voluntary emission reduction market, resulting in the emergence of China Certified Emission Reduction (hereinafter referred to as "CCER"). CCER encourages social subjects to take emission reduction actions and participate in the construction of emission reduction projects, so as to effectively reduce greenhouse gas emissions. On the other hand, it will activate market trading vitality, promote innovation in carbon financial derivatives, and support industries in accelerating green and low-carbon transformation.

In general, the domestic voluntary emission reduction mechanisms dominated by "CCER" and "carbon inclusion mechanism" are a new long-term incentive measure for energy conservation and carbon reduction, a strong supplement to the mandatory carbon market, and an important part of the multilevel carbon market structure. While promoting urban development, all regions should also actively respond to the national goals of carbon peak and carbon neutrality, continuously optimize the industrial and energy consumption structure, improve the ability to save energy, reduce carbon emissions and increase efficiency, encourage industries and enterprises to optimize their operation modes and innovate business modules, guide key emission units to complete mandatory emission reduction tasks with quality and quantity guaranteed, and encourage the public to actively participate in voluntary emission reduction markets, so that everyone in our cities can extensively and deeply participate in green emission reduction activities and effectively promote the coordinated development of urbanization and ecological environment quality improvement.

Chapter II

Urban Governance and Resilient Development

Interdisciplinary Research on Future Cities and Transportation Systems

Zhang Junyi
Chair Professor, School of Transportation, Southeast University, China Fellow, The Engineering Academy of Japan

This is an excerpt from the author's speech at the special forum themed "Sustainable Transport and the Future of Cities".

Future urban development presents both challenges and opportunities, shaped by numerous unpredictable factors. As a crucial component of cities, the advancement of transportation systems must be intricately aligned with urban planning. Cities and their transportation networks are interwoven entities with complex internal and external relationships, necessitating insights from various disciplines. To gain a comprehensive understanding of the interplay between urban environments and transportation systems, and to guide their holistic development, interdisciplinary research should be actively encouraged.

1 Interdisciplinary Research

Interdisciplinary research differs fundamentally from multidisciplinary research. Multidisciplinary research involves researchers from multiple fields working together, each applying their distinct disciplinary knowledge to tackle a single issue. This often results in a straightforward "1+1=2" effect, where the sum of the parts is simply additive. In contrast, interdisciplinary research seeks to blend insights from different disciplines to achieve a "1+1>2" outcome, where the integration of knowledge creates new, synergistic insights. The ultimate aim of this approach is to develop a cohesive knowledge framework that transcends individual disciplines, culminating in a novel, comprehensive understanding that is greater than the sum of its parts (Transdisciplinary).

2 Reflection on Future Development Goals: Harmonized Development Goals (HDGs)

The author has dedicated decades to interdisciplinary research focused on transportation, examining its interconnections with urban development, lifestyle, energy, environment, tourism, health, and other factors. The accumulated research highlights the complex interactions and causal relationships among these elements. Given the accelerating global urbanization and the increasing severity of environmental and resource consumption issues, understanding the intricate relationship between transportation and urbanization has become increasingly crucial. Long-term planning for cities and transportation systems should extend beyond national contexts to a global scale, integrating Sustainable Development Goals (SDGs) to design systems that enhance people's quality of life while maintaining environmental balance. Interdisciplinary research into future cities and transportation systems can not only address these challenges but also provide innovative solutions from new perspectives to adapt to the evolving dynamics of urban development.

In today's increasingly unstable world, it is essential to thoughtfully consider the direction in which the post-SDGs era should evolve. Since 2015, the concept of "Planetary Health" has garnered widespread attention. Planetary health refers to the "health of human civilization and the state of the natural systems on which it depends" (Whitmee et al., 2015). However, using the term "health" to describe the future direction of global development has its limitations. Given the significance of global social health development, the author proposes redefining planetary health as the "co-health" of individuals, societies, and nature. This broader concept captures the comprehensive impact of interactions between humans and natural systems. While this expanded definition helps elucidate the essence of planetary health, it still falls short of addressing specific development goals required to tackle diverse global challenges.

Moreover, when considering future development directions, it is crucial to focus not only on international trends but also on the specific issues and development models of individual countries. This requires deep reflection and innovation to explore broader future development goals. Given the widespread and profound impacts of global risks such as geopolitical tensions, regional conflicts, and cultural clashes, the author boldly proposes that the next global development goal should be Harmonized Development Goals (HDGs), emphasizing a shift from sustainable development to harmonized development (Zhang, 2020) (Fig. 1). HDGs advocate for achieving balance and synergy across multiple dimensions, including economic growth, social progress, environmental sustainability, and cultural diversity. They promote mutual understanding and cooperation between nations and stakeholders to foster global peaceful coexistence and shared prosperity. Based on the above consideration, tra-

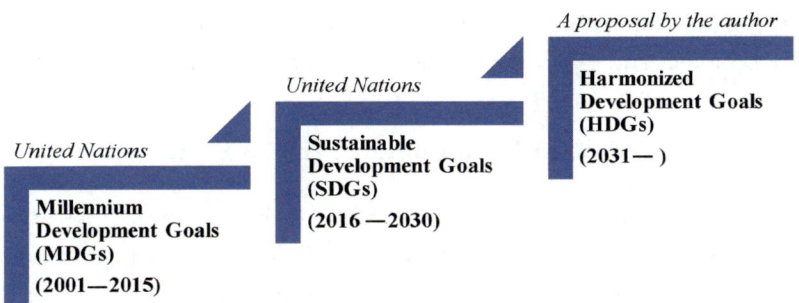

Fig. 1　Future Development Goals

ditional classifications of countries as developed or developing also warrant reconsideration. Instead, countries could be categorized according to their degrees of harmonized development (e.g., well-harmonized vs. less-harmonized). GDP no longer comprehensively reflects a country's development status, and income levels cannot fully capture the quality of development. While categorizing based on harmonious development presents both challenges and complexities compared to GDP-based classifications, it offers a more nuanced approach to assessing development.

3 Reflection on the Future Development Science: Harmonized Development Science

The essence of things or phenomena is "change", which means that all events and occurrences are transient. Once a "sustainable" state is achieved, it is inevitably followed by an "unsustainable" state. In contrast, harmony is a dynamic process that maintains balance between these states, acknowledging their continuous alternation (Fig. 2). Harmony also involves seeking balance between problem-solving solutions and their side effects, or among various solutions themselves. In summary, harmony is not a static condition but a dynamic process that integrates multiple elements into a cohesive whole. It transcends sustainability by embracing the transition process, accommodating diversity, and reducing conflict to ensure dynamic equilibrium, representing a non-reductionist perspective.

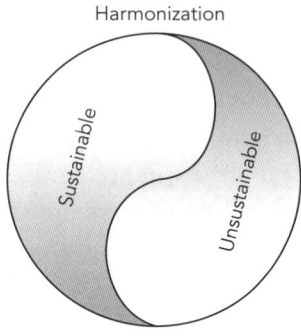

Fig. 2 "Harmony" is a State of Dynamic Equilibrium

From the perspective of harmonized development, both human society and the natural world are complex systems composed of multiple elements. These systems share common processes and mechanisms, resulting in collective behaviors that emerge from individual actions. The human system is integral to the natural system, and vice versa, indicating that they are interconnected and cannot be considered in isolation. A comprehensive understanding of both systems is therefore essential. Additionally, because of the interactions between human and natural systems, a theoretical framework that reflects these interactions is crucial for a complete understanding of either system. The author refers to this integrative scientific approach as Harmonized Development Science (Zhang, 2020). Harmonized Development Science aims to address future global societal changes and explore strategies for coexisting with these changes.

4 New Concept of Future Urban Development: HEARTY City

The development of future cities should account for both the commonalities and unique characteristics of urban environments while scientifically integrating various development concepts. Different cities encounter distinct challenges and development needs, making a multidimensional approach essential for future urban planning. Therefore, development strategies should be diverse and tailored to the specific characteristics and challenges of each city to ensure comprehensive growth and long-term prosperity.

The author proposes the HEARTY City (Fig. 3) for the future (Zhang, 2024a). In this proposal:

"H" stands for Healthy City. The concept of a healthy city emphasizes the physical, psychological, and social well-being of urban residents. By improving air quality and the built environment, promoting healthy lifestyles, and enhancing medical services, the goal is to create an environment that supports residents' comprehensive health and well-being.

"E" refers to Eco-City or Energy-saving City, which emphasizes ecological balance and efficient resource utilization. Measures such as ecological planning, urban greening, and water resource management are implemented to protect natural ecosystems while improving the city's ecological quality and sustainability.

"A" represents AI-driven City, i.e., smart city. It leverages artificial intelligence and other technologies to optimize urban management and public services, thereby enhancing residents' quality of life and improving the efficiency of urban operations.

"R" stands for Resilient City, which aims to enhance a city's adaptability to natural disasters, economic challenges, or social issues. A resilient city emphasizes building resilient infrastructure, promoting disaster management, and risk reduction measures to ensure sustainable urban development.

"T" stands for Tourism City. A tourism city is characterized by its attractiveness, diversity, and vitality, capable of drawing numerous visitors while managing and balancing the impacts and challenges associated with tourism development.

"Y" refers to Yearning City. The yearning city emphasizes a balance between natural, cultural, and social development, fostering a unique allure and pleasant living environment that inspires residents' deep attachment and emotional connection to the

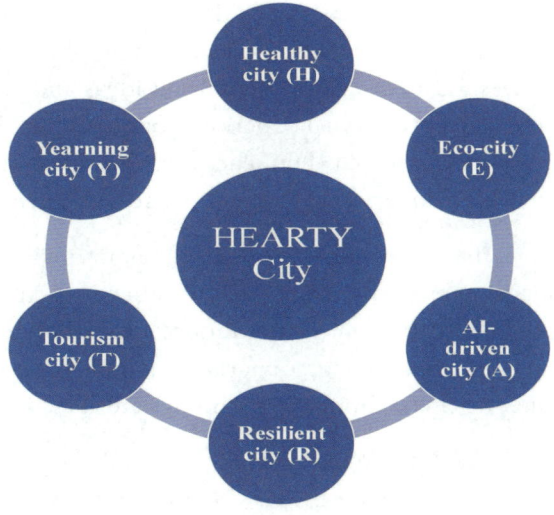

Fig. 3   HEARTY City

Chapter II Urban Governance and Resilient Development

city, creating a distinctive urban image and brand.

The above six urban development concepts described are interconnected, exhibiting both contradictions and synergies. For example, in an AI-Driven City (A), disruptions in digital networks might undermine its Resilience (R). Conversely, efforts to build Resilient Cities (R) could unintentionally detract from the city's natural beauty, potentially diminishing its appeal or Yearning (Y). The objectives of an Eco-City (E) might also conflict with the economic goals promoted by an AI-Driven City (A). Additionally, over-tourism in a Tourism City (T) could reduce the city's peaceful and harmonious qualities or Yearning (Y).

However, integrating these concepts can yield mutually beneficial outcomes. For instance, an AI-Driven City (A) can enhance the resilience of its infrastructure (R). Resilient Cities should prioritize nature-friendly solutions (R), which can preserve natural landscapes and enhance residents' Yearning for natural beauty (Y). Eco-Cities (E) and AI can coexist harmoniously if aligned with natural systems. A Yearning City (Y) may attract more tourists, potentially evolving into a vibrant Tourism City (T), with over-tourism issues possibly mitigated by AI-driven solutions (A). Finally, the principles of an Eco-City (E) can support the creation of Healthy (H) and Yearning (Y) cities by reducing reliance on new construction.

5 New Science of Future Urban Development: Urbanimmunology

To grasp the complexity of urban and transportation systems, the author emphasizes the importance of integrating technological and theoretical innovations. Technological innovations rely on solid theoretical foundations, while new theoretical innovations are the cornerstone of future development. Here, the author boldly introduces the concept of Urbanimmunology, new discipline to understand the capacities that a city can protect itself by resisting to disruptions and adapt to disruptions, and to develop responses that can help the city to enhance its immunity level and consequently, to evolve into a resilient system. (Zhang, 2024b) (Fig. 4). Urbanimmunology represents the intersection of immunology and urban science, aiming to deepen our understanding of cities and improve their adaptability to various challenges. This approach reflects on urban development practices, emphasizing that valuable lessons should be retained. Despite accumulating significant ideas and experiences, cities often revert to previous states after initial experimentation. Urban development should not consist of temporary changes but should actively assimilate, integrate, and sustain effective practices to ensure long-term adaptability and resilience.

During the pandemic, the author drew inspiration from human immunology to propose a process management methodology applicable to general policies, known as the DIRECT Approach (Detect, Inform, React, Enforce, Collaborate, Transfer) (Zhang, 2021; Zhang, 2022). This methodology remarkably parallels the functions of components such as lymphocytes in the human immune system (Fig. 5).

- Detect (D): By studying the role of epithelial cells and phagocytes' Toll-like receptors (TLRs), continuously monitor the city for anomalies (urban issues being analo-

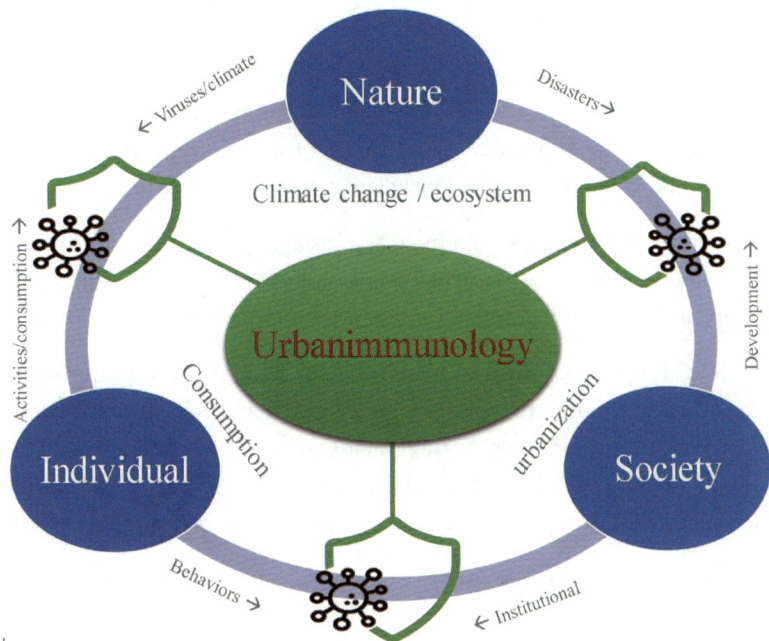

Fig. 4　Urbanimmunology

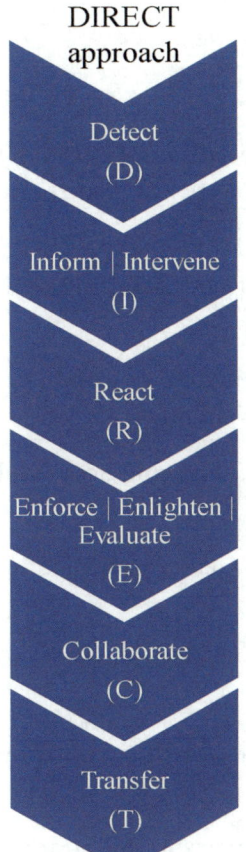

Fig. 5　DIRECT Approach

gous to invasive pathogens).

- Inform (I): Based on the role of T lymphocytes activated by phagocytes, inform the city's immune system about detected anomalies. T lymphocytes are selected and graded in the thymus. Most selected and graded lymphocytes do not misidentify themselves as enemies and are skilled at recognizing threats.

- React (R): Stakeholders responsible for urban elements respond appropriately to detected anomalies and address them by learning the role of antibodies specifically designed for invasive pathogens. Antibodies are produced by B lymphocytes released by T lymphocytes.

- Enforce (E): Investigate the impacts of detected anomalies thoroughly by understanding the role of cytotoxic T lymphocytes that receive antigenic information from dendritic cells, attach to infected and cancer cells and eliminate them, and strengthen various measures to prevent the recurrence.

- Collaborate (C): Stakeholders collaborate to address various urban issues by leveraging the roles of different immune cells responsible for diverse aspects

Chapter II　Urban Governance and Resilient Development

of immunity.

- Transfer (T): Experience gained through the above complex process (acquired immunity) is transferred to address the next anomaly. Acquired immunity is complementary to natural immunity. With the acquired immunity, previous invasive pathogens will be remembered and attacked when they invade the body next time.

The DIRECT approach emphasizes effective management and continuous optimization during implementation, demonstrating the potential and insights provided by the integration of theory and practice in urban development.

Based on DIRECT approach and in combination with the Kaya identity of carbon emission, the author further proposes a six-domain and six-step approach for formulating and implementing integrated policies of carbon emission reduction in the transport sector (Zhang, 2021; Zhang, 2022). First, modifying the Kaya identity for the transport sector, six domains to achieve carbon emission reduction are proposed:

(1) Reducing carbon intensity of energy consumption from transport

(2) Reducing energy consumption from transport

(3) Reducing transport pressures from life and business activities

(4) Reducing high-carbon life and business activities

(5) Changing the needs in life and business

(6) Population policy

For each domain, the policy process management method based on DIRECT approach is proposed, forming a 6x6 policy matrix. The six specific DIRECT steps are as follows:

(1) D: Detect — Investigate and identify the current carbon emission issues and challenges.

(2) I: Inform | Intervene — Promote awareness and implementation of carbon reduction goals through effective communication and policy intervention.

(3) R: React — Respond promptly and adjust policies to address changing needs and conditions.

(4) E: Enlighten | Enforce | Evaluate — Educate and strengthen policies, and continuously assess and improve carbon reduction outcomes.

(5) C: Collaborate — Facilitate cooperation among government agencies, society, and businesses to achieve common carbon reduction goals.

(6) T: Transfer — Ensure the long-term stability and continuity of carbon reduction policies and practices.

The six-domain and six-step approach provides a systematic framework for addressing carbon emission issues, with the potential to advance the comprehensive implementation of the carbon neutrality goal.

6 New Theory of Life Behavior: Life-oriented Approach

Transportation is a fundamental aspect of daily life, with various behaviors intertwining and interacting to become defining features of modern society. Consequently, the author introduced the Life-Oriented Approach (Zhang, 2017). This approach emphasizes analyzing and understanding the interdependence between life choices, highlighting the interactions across different areas of life. It posits that while life choices influence transportation behaviors, transportation behaviors also play a crucial role in shaping life choices. These perspectives are supported by both theoretical foundations and empirical research (Fig. 6).

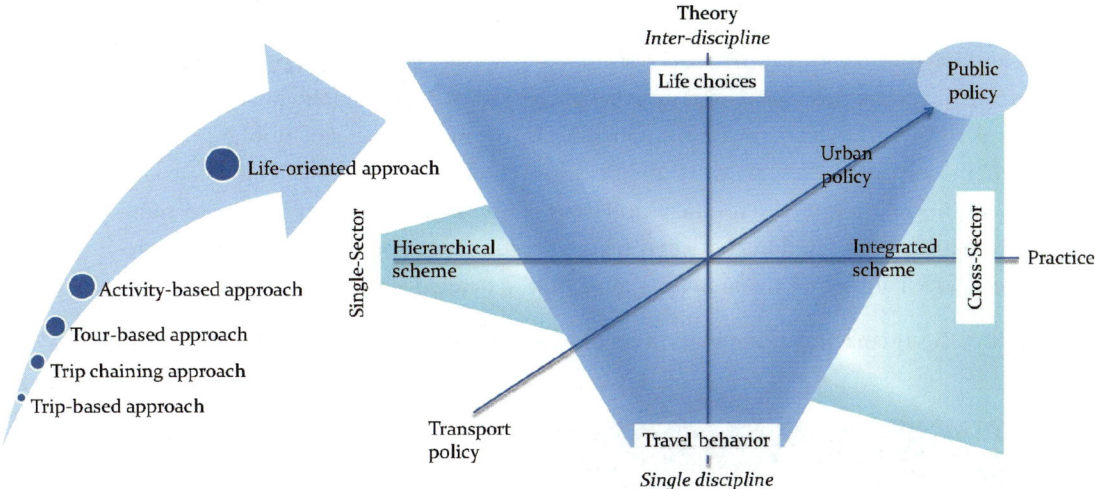

Fig. 6 Life-oriented Approach

In practice, the Life-Oriented Approach highlights the importance of deep communication and collaboration across sectors to ensure mutual understanding and coordinated action. It offers a new theoretical foundation for developing cross-sectoral urban and regional policies and serves as an innovative framework for advancing comprehensive public policies. As an interdisciplinary theoretical system, the Life-Oriented Approach has the potential to act as a common language for enhancing cross-sectoral decision-making and policy coordination.

Its core concept is to thoroughly understand and address the complex interactions between different aspects of life through systematic analysis and holistic thinking. The methodology emphasizes solving practical issues and maximizing social benefits, with the goal of fostering sustainable development and overall management improvements. By applying this comprehensive approach, the Life-Oriented Approach not only facilitates coordinated development across various social sectors but also enhances the effectiveness and adaptability of public policies, thereby providing strong support for societal progress and improvement.

7 New Theory of Transportation Development: Transport-in-All-Policies Approach

The transportation system has a direct impact on people's lifestyles, economic activities, and overall societal efficiency. For instance, smooth traffic flow is crucial for travel convenience and time management, which significantly influences economic development and social prosperity. Although transportation experts might not always be central to public policy formulation, their influence on socio-economic and environmental systems is substantial. In modern society, transportation is intricately connected with the economy, social development, health, environment, ecology, and culture, reflecting a web of interdependencies and causal relationships.

Addressing transportation issues requires considering not only the internal dynamics of transportation systems but also the broader impact of external factors. Solutions must address both the fundamental and practical aspects of transportation, both within and beyond the transportation system itself. To tackle these deep-seated issues, the author proposes the "Transport-in-All-Policies" (TiAP) approach (Zhang, 2024c). TiAP aims to integrate transportation considerations into all areas of public policy to comprehensively address societal transportation challenges (Fig. 7). This approach stresses the need for interdisciplinary and cross-departmental collaboration to manage the complex interrelations between transportation, economic activities, social development, environmental sustainability, and public health.

To support the theoretical framework and practical application of the TiAP approach,

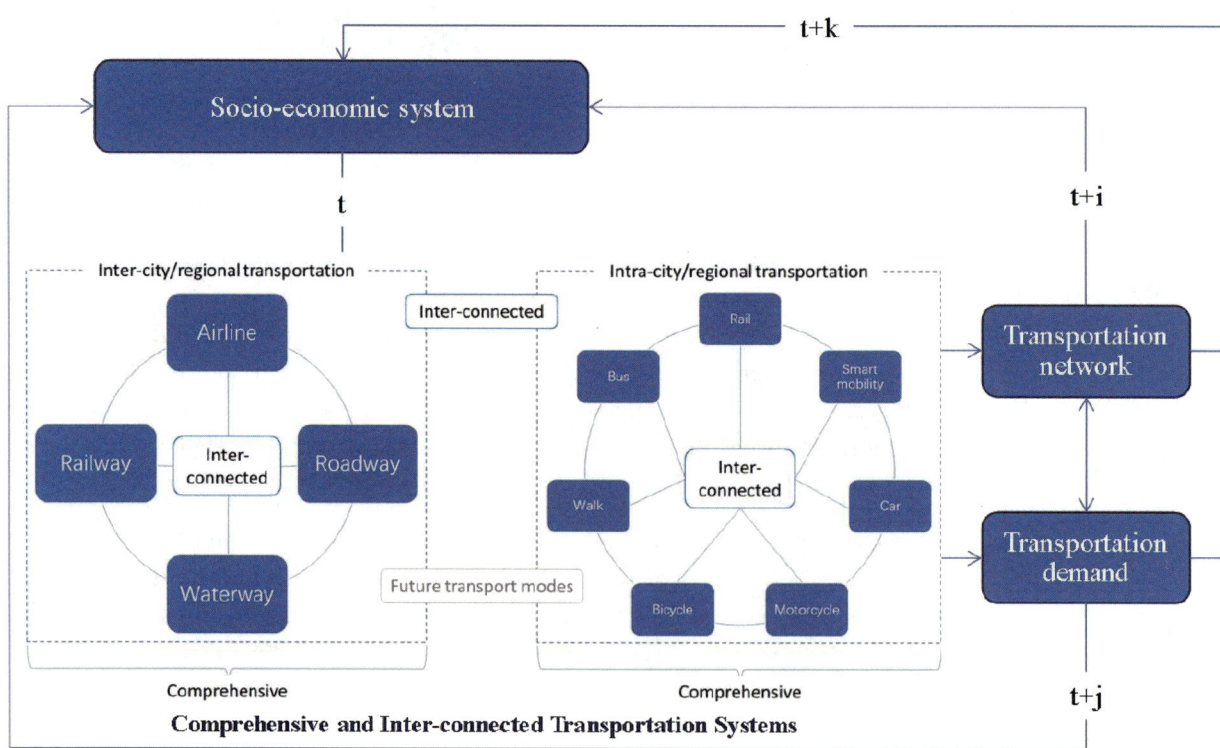

six guiding principles are proposed: the principle of common vision, the principle of evidence-based policymaking, the principle of comprehensiveness, the principle of coherence, the principle of networked governance, and the participatory principle. These principles will not only clarify the role and impact of transportation systems on socio-economic development but also provide concrete strategies for addressing current transportation challenges. They offer both theoretical support and practical guidance for public policy-making, ensuring effective implementation and continuous improvement of policies.

8 Summary

The integrated development of future cities and transportation systems is essential and necessitates the active involvement of researchers from various disciplines. Given the global uncertainties and instabilities, the advancement of cities and transportation systems must adopt a global perspective and promote innovative ideas for multi-departmental collaboration. This shift requires a seamless integration of theoretical and technological innovations to address the increasingly complex urban challenges and transportation demands (Fig. 8).

Based on extensive interdisciplinary research and experience, the author has proposed several new concepts and theories, which are integrated as illustrated in the figure above, with the aim of stimulating deep reflection and discussion among academics and policymakers. First, the Harmonized Development Goals (HDGs) are designed to set specific and ambitious targets for global future development. Second, Harmonized Development Science emphasizes the balance and coordination among various elements in the development process. The HEARTY City concept integrates multiple factors such as health, ecology, energy efficiency, artificial intelligence, urban resilience, tourism, and aspiration to explore the multi-dimensional balance of urban development.

Urbanimmunology focuses on the stability and adaptability of urban systems, addressing not only emergency responses but also long-term future development. The policy management process theory, i.e., DIRECT Approach, and the Life-Oriented Approach both emphasize effective management in policy implementation and the understanding and guidance of life behaviors, respectively. Meanwhile, the "Transport-in-All-Policies (TiAP)" approach advocates integrating transportation factors into all areas of public policy to achieve coordinated development and sustainable management across different domains.

These concepts and theoretical methods not only provide new ideas and frameworks for the integrated development of cities and transportation systems but also offer theoretical support and practical guidance for address-

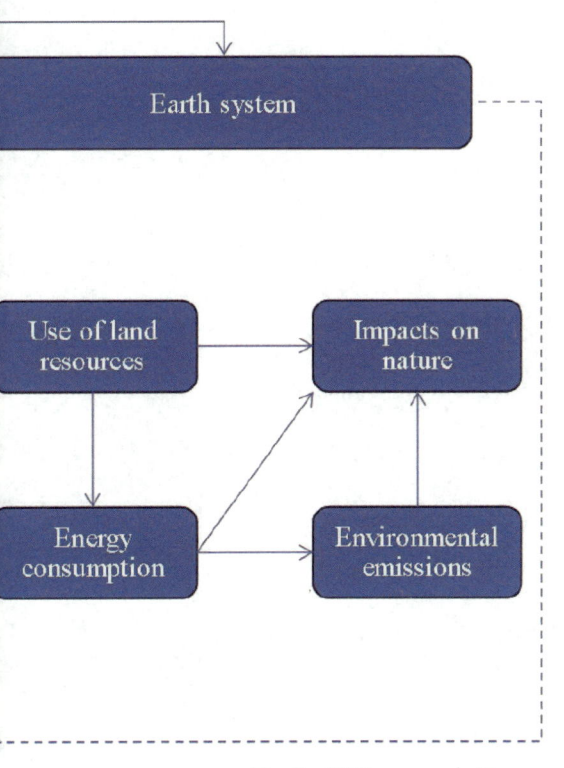

Fig. 7 TiAP approach (Transport-in-All-Policies approach)

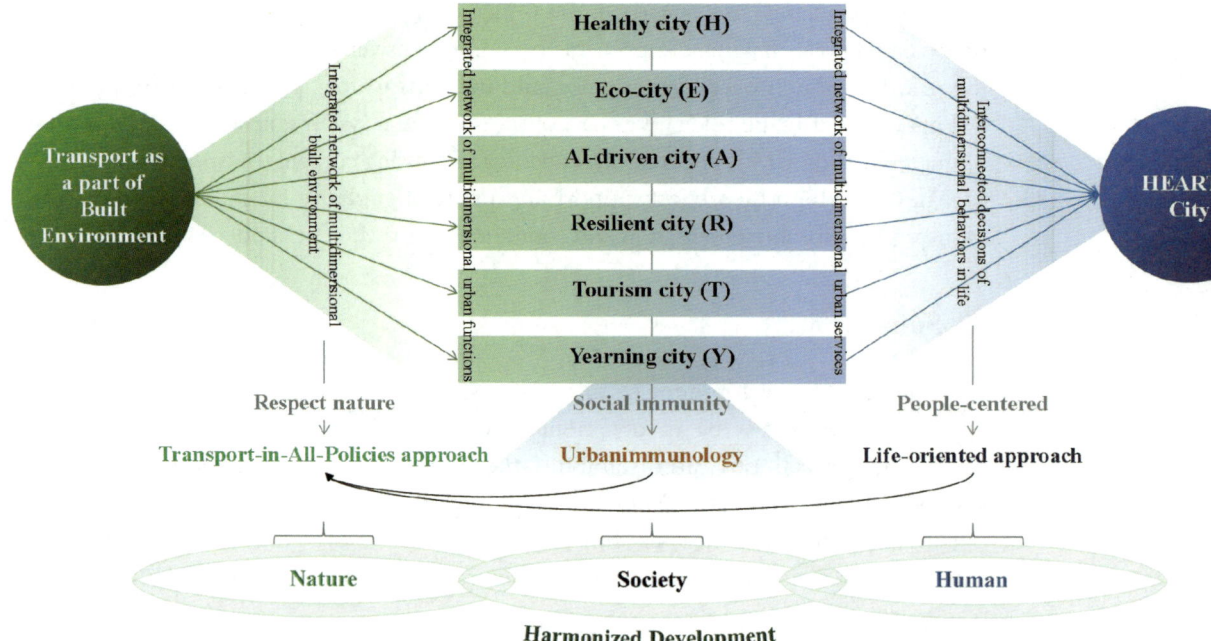

Fig. 8 Interdisciplinary Research Framework of Future Cities and Transportation Systems

ing global challenges and promoting human well-being. Through in-depth research, dissemination, and application of results, they contribute to building smarter and more sustainable cities and transportation systems, laying a scientific foundation for the advancement and development of future societies.

References

1. Whitmee S., Haines, A., Beyrer C., et al. (2015) Safeguarding human health in the Anthropocene epoch: report of The Rockefeller Foundation—Lancet Commission on planetary health. The Lancet, 386 (10007), 1973-2028.
2. Zhang J. (2017) Life-oriented Behavioral Research for Urban Policy. Springer.
3. Zhang J. (2020) Harmonization Science (HarS): From Sustainability to Harmonization. https://home.hiroshima-u.ac.jp/~zjy/wp-content/uploads/2021/10/Harmonization-Science_Proposed-in-Sept-2020-2.pdf.
4. Zhang J. Y. (2021) Integrated carbon reduction policies on transportation in the era of post-Covid-19. Urban Transport of China, 19(5), 43-52.
5. Zhang J. (2022) Governance for post-COVID-19 carbon reduction: A case study of the transport sector. In: Zhang J. and Hayashi Y. (eds.), Transportation Amid Pandemics: Lessons Learned from COVID-19, Chapter 34, Elsevier.
6. Zhang J. (2024a) HEARTY City. In: Zhang J. et al. (2024) COVID-19 & Pandemics, Lifestyles, Human Mobilities, and Cities: A Perspective of Planetary Health. Springer.
7. Zhang J. (2024b) Urbanimmunology. In: Zhang J. et al. (2024) COVID-19 & Pandemics, Lifestyles, Human Mobilities, and Cities: A Perspective of Planetary Health. Springer.
8. Zhang J. (2024c) Transport-in-All-Policies approach. In: Zhang J. et al., Research Handbook on Transport and COVID-19. Edward Elgar Publishing.

ESG Ratings for China's Urban Development

Chiu, Tzu-Kuan
PhD in finance, Wharton School, University of Pennsylvania; Professor of Finance, Shanghai Advanced Institute of Finance, Academic Director of Sustainable Finance, Shanghai Jiao Tong University

This is an excerpt from the author's speech at the "2023 Global Cities Forum".

Recently, Forbes China released the "Forbes China · Cities with Consumption Vitality in 2023", with Beijing, Shanghai, Guangzhou, and Chongqing ranking top with excellent performance in business maturity, consumption vibrancy, and transportation convenience. The results are quite interesting and reflect the "bustling" nature of modern cities. When a city has advantages in location, transportation, market, technology, and policies, it can provide inclusive and diversified consumption services for the people, forming a vibrant center.

Consumption vitality is not the only indicator for us to evaluate a city, and there are more perspectives. In fact, my research team evaluates cities from the perspective of China's national 2035 vision. The indicators include the conceptual framework of the Sustainable Development Goals (SDGs) and the content of Environmental, Social, and Governance (ESG), thereby forming an evaluation framework to rate the ESG governance of Chinese cities and analyze the results.

This research project was jointly initiated by Zhang Bohui, Wu Haifeng, and I in 2021. Although it was interrupted due to the COVID-19 pandemic, the final results have been compiled into *ESG Ratings for China's Urban Development*, a book successfully published by China Financial Publishing House. Amidst the hot topic of the "List of Cities with Consumption Vitality", my research team takes the opportunity to share with readers the city rankings from the perspective of the national vision.

1 ESG Rating Categories

As its name suggests, this book involves ESG ratings. In recent years, ESG ratings have garnered significant attention in China, but the focus has been primarily on corporate ratings. This book takes "cities" as the subject of evaluation, and I will first clarify the concept of ESG ratings.

ESG ratings refer to a rating framework established by the rater, whereby the performance of the rated subjects is evaluated based on issues in the E, S, and G aspects, and scores are then assigned accordingly. ESG ratings do not necessarily involve rankings, but since the rated subjects will have varying scores, some ESG rating organizations may rank the rated subjects based on their scores.

ESG ratings can be classified into three levels: macro, meso, and micro. The rated subjects and the ESG issues of concern vary accordingly. Macro-level ESG ratings evaluate countries, with issues of concern including per capita carbon emissions (E), income inequality (S), and compliance with international conventions (G); meso-level ESG ratings evaluate cities, with issues of concern including urban air quality (E), the urban employment rate (S), and urban governance (G); micro-level ESG ratings evaluate companies, with issues of concern including product carbon footprint (E), supply chain management (S), and financial transparency (G).

In the real world, the number of institutions engaged in macro, meso, and micro-level ESG ratings varies greatly. This is because some rating results are for commercial applications. The rating results can form ESG databases, and as ESG-focused investment has surged, the market demand for corporate ESG data is high. In contrast, the demand for city and country-level ESG rating data is relatively lacking, which has dampened the motivation of rating agencies to participate.

2 Concept of ESG Ratings for Urban Development

Among the three categories, the ESG rating system developed by my team is focused on the meso level, aiming to integrate the guiding principles of China's 2035 Vision dynamically, the SDG conceptual framework in public management, and the core elements of ESG. This allows the identification of the critical drivers of urban sustainable development and the establishment of a comprehensive assessment system for evaluating city-level ESG governance.

According to the *Outline of the 14th Five-Year Plan (2021—2025) for National Economic and Social Development and the Long-Range Objectives Through the Year 2035* ("the Outline" for short), since China has transitioned from high-speed development to high-quality development, the focus of economic and social development in the next five years should be on deepening reform and opening-up, improving social civilization, building an ecological civilization, enhancing people's livelihood, and raising the level of national governance. The goals include perfecting the mechanism for technological innovation, promoting the shift from virtual to real industrial development, establishing a fair distribution mechanism for social wealth, giving full play to the strategic support role of the state-owned economy, advancing green development, and striving to achieve the "30/60" decarbonization goal.

The SDGs were proposed by the United Nations in 2015 as part of the "2030 Agenda for Sustainable Development", addressing 17 pressing challenges facing humanity. These 17 goals target macro-level ESG issues, such as Climate Action (SDG #13) and Life Below Water (SDG #14) under the "E" dimension, No Poverty (SDG #1) and

Gender Equality (SDG #5) under the "S" dimension, and Peace, Justice and Strong Institutions (SDG #16) and Partnerships for the Goals (SDG #17) under the "G" dimension. Therefore, the main exploration of my team is how to further incorporate ESG elements based on the sustainable development analysis in the public management field with Chinese characteristics, and refine the scoring indicators in conjunction with the Outline.

The Outline states that by 2035, China will have basically achieved socialist modernization, with five key focus areas: economic development, driving innovation, people's wellbeing, green ecology, and security assurance. The development priorities of the Outline are generally consistent with the United Nations' 2030 Agenda, but the former is formulated based on China's current historical stage, and thus has characteristics tailored to the local context, differing in some details from the SDGs. My team has mapped the five development directions proposed in the "Outline" to the SDGs, as shown in Tab. 1:

Tab. 1 Relations between major development directions proposed in the Outline and SDGs

Development directions proposed in the Outline	17 SDGs (No. #)
Economic Development	No Poverty (SDG #1), Decent Work and Economic Growth (SDG #8) Reduced Inequalities (SDG #10), Peace, Justice and Strong Institutions (SDG #16)
Innovation-driven	Industry, Innovation, and Infrastructure (SDG #9), Responsible Consumption and Production (SDG #12), Partnerships for the Goals (SDG #17)
People's Well-being	Good Health and Well-being (SDG #3), Quality Education (SDG #4), Gender Equality (SDG #5) Affordable and Clean Energy (SDG #7), Sustainable Cities and Communities (SDG #11)
Green Ecology	Climate Action (SDG #13), Life below Water (SDG #14), Life on Land (SDG #15)
Safety Guarantee	Zero Hunger (SDG #2), Clean Water and Sanitation (SDG #6)

After aligning the main development directions proposed in the Outline with SDGs, it is necessary to assign ESG content to them so as to form specific indicators. This involves the construction of a rating framework and the establishment of mathematical methods.

3　Rating Framework and Methododology

There are three keys to the rating, namely scope, measurement and weight. Scope refers to what is covered by the rating, measurement refers to how the rating is measured, and weight refers to the relative importance of each indicator of the rating. The following is a brief description in sequence.

First, the coverage of the urban vision rating is undoubtedly further endowed with ESG content based on the relationship in Tab. 1, which involves the construction of a hierarchical ESG indicator system, including Level I, Level II and Level III indicators. Here, Level I indicators are also called drivers and have the highest abstraction. Level II indicators often define the contents of Level I indicators by listing attributes, thus reducing their abstractness. Level III indicators further materialize Level II indicators to interface with the observable empirical world for data extraction.

The Urban Vision Rating System adopts a hierarchical rating system, which includes Level I, Level II and Level III indicators. There are 5 Level I indicators, namely urban government governance efficiency, urban economic development, urban ecological civilization construction, urban people's livelihood and wellbeing construction and urban civilization construction.

They are the driving force of urban ESG development. There are 22 Level II indicators under the Level I indicator and 76 Level III indicators under the Level II indicator. The Urban Vision Rating System is formed by these hierarchical indicators.

For example, the Level I indicator "urban government governance efficiency" has 3 Level II indicators, namely "construction of urban socialist democracy and rule of law" "role and credibility of urban government" and "urban emergency response capacity". There are 11 Level III indicators under the Level II indicator, namely "Number of lawyers per 10,000 people" "number of property right dispute cases" "number of urban legislation" "rate of administrative litigation cases" "proportion of poverty alleviation expenditure in fiscal revenue" "government anti-corruption situation" "proportion of direct income tax in tax revenue" "financial security capacity" "integrity benefit" "proportion of public security expenditure in fiscal revenue" and "comprehensive self-sufficiency ability of grain". These Level III indicators are expressed in the form of quantity, benefit and proportion, thus forming the measurement variables for drawing data.

After defining the indicators at all levels, the author's team still has to decide on the measurement method and weight configuration before carrying out the rating work. Regarding the measurement method, in fact, it can be seen from the proportion and quantity in the above indicator expression that the urban vision rating adopts quantitative measurement. The data is mainly based on actual statistical data and supplemented by estimated data. Sources include statistical yearbooks of various cities, Foresight Database, Wind Database, National Bureau of Statistics, Drcnet.com.cn, etc. Regarding the weight, the urban vision rating adopts the equal weight method for all levels of indicators, indicating that their importance is the same.

In terms of index method, the urban vision rating is compiled by conventional multi-index mathematical composite method. After the rating framework and method are clarified, the author's team must carry out necessary processing such as dimensionless data before evaluating China's urban vision practices. The rating is based on a sample of 39 cities in China from 2009 to 2019, including 4 first-tier cities.

15 new first-tier cities, 17 provincial capitals and 3 municipalities with independent planning status.

4 Rating Results and Policy Implications

The rating results can be judged by the scores of comprehensive indicators or indicators at all levels. The comprehensive indicator is formed by summarizing Level I indicators, and its score represents the comprehensive performance of 5 Level I indicators. Due to limited space, this paper mainly analyzes the comprehensive indicator score ranking.

Cities with high comprehensive indicator scores are basically distributed in the form of urban agglomeration, showing obvious agglomeration effect and imbalance. In this regard, the author's team has conducted in-depth analysis on the advantages of core cities, outward radiation effects and challenges behind coordinated development for Beijing-Tianjin-Hebei Economic Development Zone dominated by Beijing and Tianjin, Yangtze River Delta Economic Development Zone dominated by Shanghai, Hangzhou and Nanjing, and Pearl River Delta Economic Development Zone dominated by cities in Guangdong-Hong Kong-Macao Greater Bay Area.

Based on the comprehensive scores of 39 cities, we can rank them and the results are shown in Fig. 1. The top six are Beijing, Shanghai, Guangzhou, Shenzhen, Chongqing and Tianjin. Beijing scored 185.79, far ahead of the second-place city Shanghai (152.77).

A closer look at Fig. 1 reveals that firstly, the comprehensive scores of the top six cities show an obvious ladder shape with a large gap between the scores of each city, but starting from Wuhan, the seventh-place city, the gap in comprehensive scores gradually narrowed. Secondly, the comprehensive score of cities shows the agglomeration effect, that is, the core city in a region drives the development of surrounding secondary cities with its radiation power.

Thirdly, the comprehensive score of cities reflects many imbalances between first-tier and non-first-tier cities, special economic zone cities and non-special economic zone cities, and eastern coastal cities and non-eastern coastal cities. These findings show that in addition to the imbalance between urban and rural development, there is a serious problem of regional unbalanced development in China. These findings are

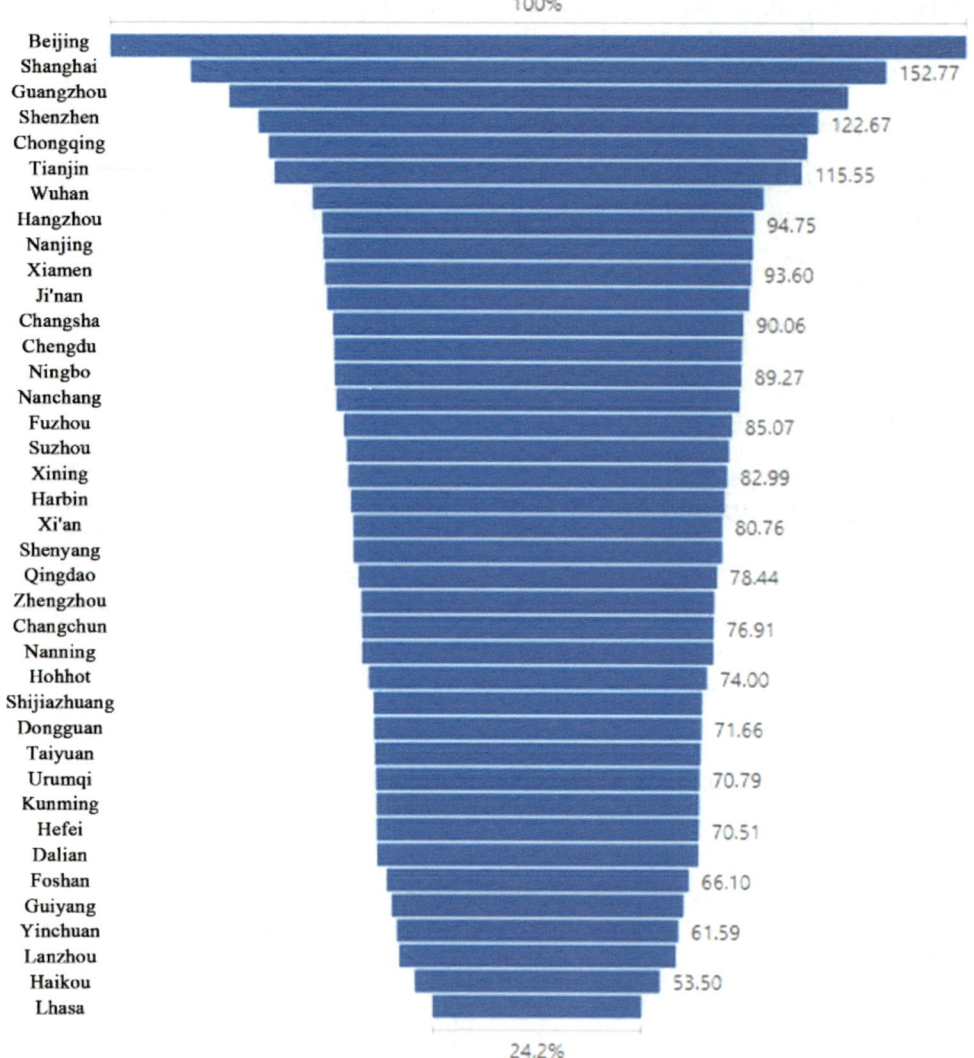

Fig. 1　Comprehensive scores of 39 cities

more informative for the governments to address the challenges and promote policies that better balance development between regions.

According to the planning of the author's team, the urban vision practice rating work is divided into 3 stages. The first stage is to sort out the rating concept, build the framework, collect data and carry out the rating. This part of the work has been completed because of the release of scores for 39 cities and the analysis of factors behind them. The second stage is to expand the research ideas to the whole country, so as to form a report on the practice of national urban vision. The third stage is to build a data visualization platform, where the collected and sorted-out data of various places are placed for inquiry by all parties involved in industry, government and university. Such a centralized data collection and query platform will improve information transparency, facilitate government policy evaluation and enterprise strategy adjustments, and have far-reaching impacts on society.

How Large Models Can Be Utilized in Urban Governance: Practices and Reflections[1]

Wu Jiannan[*]   Ma Taiping[**]   Zhou Lei[***]

[*] Executive Vice President of the China Institute for Urban Governance, Shanghai Jiao Tong University (SJTU); Dean of the School of International and Public Affairs, SJTU
[**] Doctoral Student at the School of International and Public Affairs, SJTU
[***] Doctoral Student at the School of International and Public Affairs, SJTU

This is an excerpt from the author's speech at the "2023 Global Cities Forum".

1   Introduction: How Can the Digital Transformation of Urban Governance Be Upgraded?

In November 2022, OpenAI launched ChatGPT, which gained over 100 million active users globally within two months, becoming the fastest-user-growing consumption-level application in history, thus sparking significant attention from society regarding large artificial intelligence (AI) models. In the wave of enthusiasm brought by ChatGPT, the AI industry in China quickly followed suit, intensifying efforts to develop large AI models based on the Chinese language environment. According to the *Chinese AI Large Model Map Research Report*, as of May 2023, China had seen the emergence of 79 large model products with parameters exceeding 1-billion scale.

The Chinese central government places great importance on the development of large AI models. In April 2023, the General Secretary of the Communist Party of China (CPC), Xi Jinping, while presiding over a meeting of the Political Bureau of the CPC Central Committee, emphasized the importance of developing artificial general intelligence (AGI), fostering an innovative ecosystem, and prioritizing risk prevention. In July 2023, the Cyberspace Administration of China, along with six other ministries and commissions, jointly issued the *Interim Measures for the Management of Generative Artificial Intelligence Services*, which further encourages the innovative application of generative AI technology across various industries and fields.

---

1 This paper is supported by the national major project Research on Mechanism and Optimization Path of Digital Transformation of Social Governance in Mega-cities (21&ZD162). Thanks to Jia Kai, Huang Hui, Feng Yu, Zhang Acheng, and Chu Zhongzhu for their advice and support.

In response to the strategic deployments at the central government level, seven cities, namely Beijing, Shenzhen, Chengdu, Hangzhou, Wuxi, Shanghai, and Chongqing, have taken the lead in introducing policies to support the development of large AI models, proposing to promote the demonstrative application of large AI models in urban governance. This article aims to address the following two questions: How can large models be used in urban governance, and what are the common characteristics of these applications? How can the digital transformation of future cities be better advanced through the application of large model application practices?

2 Analysis Basis: From AI to Large Model Technology

2.1 A brief introduction to the development history of AI Technology

In 1956, John McCarthy and nine other scientists jointly organized the Dartmouth Conference, which is widely regarded as the beginning of the development of AI technology. From the perspective of technological evolution, the development of AI can be divided into three stages: The first stage is the machine learning stage, where training was conducted according to historical data to predict the future. In this stage, the focus shifted from defining how to solve problems to finding solutions based on data learning. The second stage is the deep learning stage, where deep neural networks (DNNs) were utilized as frameworks for machine learning. This stage required larger datasets and more calculations. Compared with machine learning, deep learning can extract high-dimensional semantic features. The third stage is the basic model stage, which focused on transfer learning and scale realization. The former involves applying the "knowledge" gained from one task to another, primarily through the pre-training method. The latter emphasizes improvements in computer hardware, the development of Transformer model architectures, and the availability of increased training data.

2.2 Connotation and classification of large models

The "large" in large models refers to big data, large-value parameters, and significant computing power. From a functional perspective, large models can be mainly divided into two categories: Generative and discriminative. Discriminative AI maps high-dimensional, rich sensory input to category labels for prediction and classification; generative AI refers to AI systems that create content such as text, audio, or video, aiming to generate new and creative outputs based on training data. Discriminative AI and generative AI differ across dimensions such as task processing and application objectives, as detailed in Tab.1.

Compared with traditional AI, large models have unique technical characteristics. First, task generalization. Through the "pre-training + fine-tuning" technical approach, it is possible to handle multiple tasks, unknown tasks, and a large number of downstream tasks simultaneously. Second, the emergence of capabilities. When the amount of pre-training data exceeds a certain threshold, the model demonstrates advanced reasoning, learning adaptation, and other capabilities. Third, interactive humanization. After acquiring vast amounts of human corpus data, large models can learn human preferences and infer human intentions, possessing characteristics that

Tab. 1 Comparison of Discriminative AI and Generative AI

Dimension	Discriminant AI	Generative AI
Application Objective(s)	Primarily used to perform specific tasks	Able to handle multiple tasks
Interactive format	Makes predictive judgments based on training data	Uses training data to create new content
Training complexity	The input is usually in a fixed format, and the output contains content of pre-defined categories.	The input and output are very flexible, and the prompt design is intended to determine the best input.
Running speed	Simple for training	Complex for training
Technical shortcoming(s)	Runs at a relatively fast speed	Needs a certain response time
Task processing	Requires manual review of the results to avoid model misjudgments	Requires manual confirmation of output accuracy to avoid generating hallucinations

are somewhat similar to those of humans to some extent.

3 Practices: Comparison of News Reporting and Research Cases

3.1 Data sources and case selection

To promote the development, application, and ecosystem building of AI, seven cities—Beijing, Shenzhen, Chengdu, Hangzhou, Wuxi, Shanghai, and Chongqing—have taken the initiative to issue relevant policies tailored for the era of AI large models. This study utilizes the seven cities mentioned above as a sample frame and conducts online searches to find instances of large models applied in urban governance. Finally, this paper selects three case studies for analysis: the "city brain" in Haidian District, Beijing; the "smart visual integration perception system" in X District Shenzhen, and the "large model for urban operation and governance" in Chongqing.

3.2 Practices in the three regions

The "Haidian city brain" is a joint initiative by Baidu AI Cloud and the Haidian District People's Government of Beijing Municipality, designed to implement applications in urban governance based on the "Wenxin Yiyan" large model. This case was included in the "Top 20 Typical Cases of General AI Large Model Industry Application Scenarios in Beijing" and its operational logic is illustrated in Fig. 1.

The smart visual integration perception system in X District, Shenzhen, is a collaborative project developed by Allcam Information Technology Co., Ltd., along with academic institutions like Nanjing University and technology companies such as Huawei Technologies Co., Ltd. The system is built on Allcam's Urban Smart Vision 2.0 and integrates with the open interface service of Huawei's Pangu CV large model. Its goal is to enhance the empowering effects of big data in the digital transformation of urban governance, as illustrated in Fig. 2.

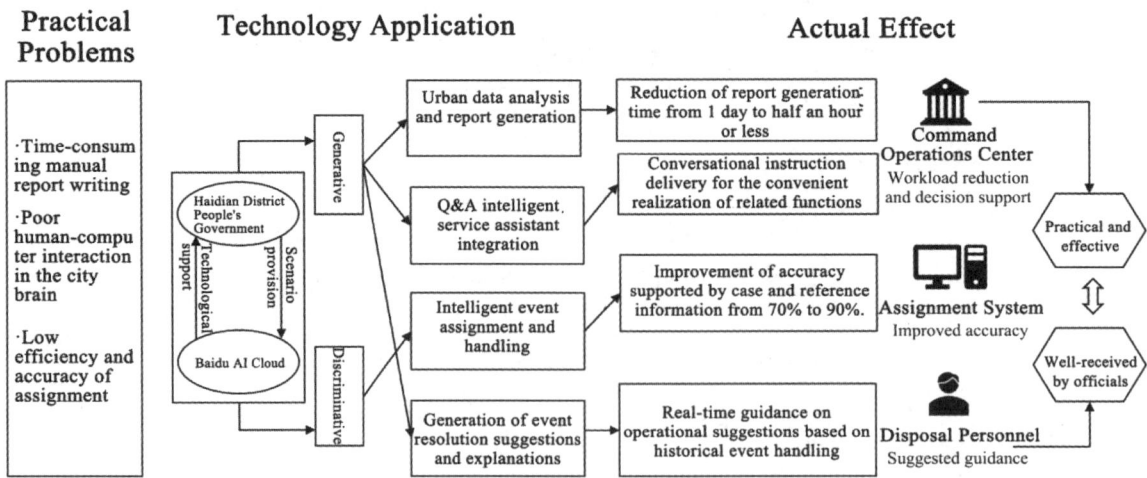

Fig. 1 Baidu AI Cloud "Haidian City Brain"

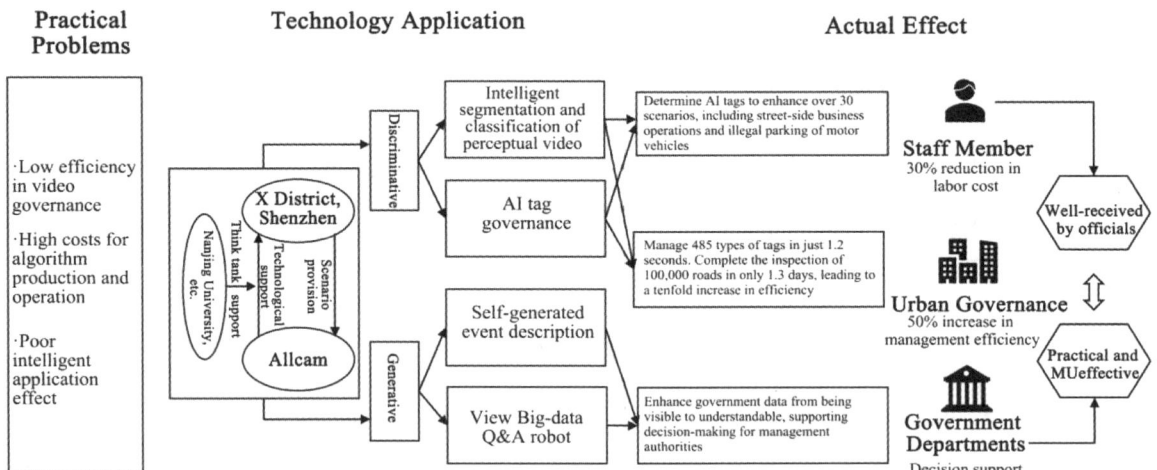

Fig. 2 Smart Visual Integration Perception System in X District, Shenzhen

In the context of the accelerated development of Digital Chongqing, the Chongqing Municipal People's Government, Digital Chongqing Company, and Alibaba Cloud have collaboratively created a large model for urban operation and governance of Chongqing. This model was unveiled at the Smart China Expo 2023. The large model is developed on Alibaba's Tongyi big model and leverages existing extensive data resources and application scenarios to enhance the efficiency of urban operation and governance, as illustrated in Fig. 3.

3.3 Common characteristics of application practice

First, there is a joint drive between generative and discriminative functions. Generative AI applications include Q&A intelligent service assistant integration, urban data analysis and report generation, generation of event resolution suggestions and explanations, as well as self-generated event description. Discriminative AI applications encompass

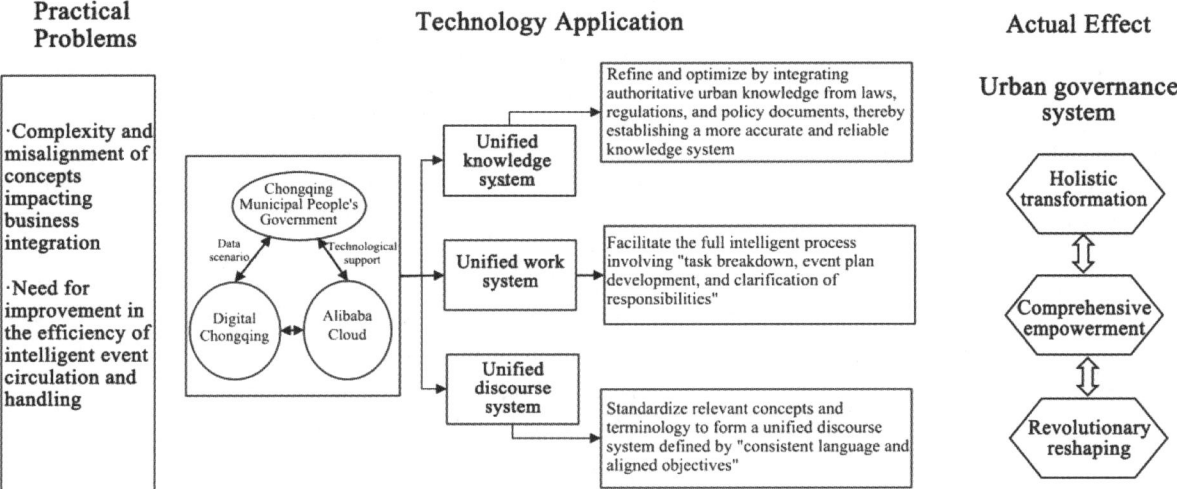

Fig. 3 Large Model for Urban Operation and Governance in Chongqing

intelligent event assignment and handling, intelligent identification, segmentation, and classification of perceptual videos, AI tag governance, and task breakdown. Second, applications are developed using general large models. All three cases leverage industry-leading general large models, incorporating authoritative urban knowledge for fine-tuning to enhance their effectiveness. Third, collaboration among government, enterprises, and society propels the application of large models. The government departments involved primarily include data management, administrative services, and urban management agencies. Each of the three cases features contributions from technology companies such as Baidu, Huawei, and Alibaba Cloud, which have developed general large models, along with research institutions that act as supporting think tanks.

4 Reflections: Where is Digital Transformation Heading in the Future

Reflecting on the past, digital transformation has generally revealed the phenomenon of "virtualization" in application scenarios, characterized by the "degradation", "large scale", and "unification" of these scenarios. Meanwhile, grassroots officials, positioned at the end of the principal-agent relationship, face multiple task demands. Rather than alleviating burdens and enhancing capabilities at the grassroots level, digital transformation has increased their burdens and diminished their effectiveness.

In the strategic context of accelerating the construction of Digital China, urban digital transformation is now entering a new stage, presenting new challenges and requirements. Specifically, there are evident disparities in development among the eastern, central, and western regions of China. In the post-pandemic era, local governments are experiencing an overall decline in financial resources, while the demand for economic development has become increasingly urgent, resulting in greater expectations for digital transformation. Looking back at the past and focusing on the present, the future of digital transformation should concentrate on three key areas.

First, we must return to our original aspiration: digital transformation is a means to solve problems and improve performance. It involves using digital technology to enhance outcomes. Digital projects should consider the operational context and associated costs. In this new historical period, projects that do not lead to performance improvements should be approached with caution, avoiding substantial financial investments. Emphasis should be placed on addressing key challenges in urban governance and better meeting the real needs of citizens.

Second, we must face the reality that stakeholders have diverse perceptions and expectations regarding new technologies and their applications. The challenges of digital transformation are largely due to these varying understandings, particularly concerning technologies like AI. Different stakeholders may approach the implementation of these technologies in unique ways, making it difficult to achieve a consensus on their applications. For example, interpretations of how large models can be utilized in urban governance differ among government departments, technology companies, media outlets, and other actors, resulting in a range of perspectives and representations in their discussions and reporting.

Third, we must emphasize collaborative development: diverse stakeholders should work together to create multidimensional value. For the central government, it is crucial to strengthen top-level design, clarify the relationship between digital transformation goals and methods, and highlight the interdependence of different stakeholders while reinforcing the institutional framework for collaborative mechanisms. City Party committees and governments should measure success based on cost, efficiency, and effectiveness, fostering innovative forms of competition and actively evaluating the applicability of various scenarios, considering management, economic, civic, and social values. Technology companies need to conduct self-assessments to ensure that their developed applications are more effective and deliver greater value. Researchers should engage deeply with the specific contexts of digital transformation, actively embrace new technologies, and collaborate further with science and engineering fields to enhance understanding and foresight.

References

1. Institute of Scientific and Technical Information of China, New Generation Artificial Intelligence Development Research Center of the Ministry of Science and Technology. Research report on AI large models in China [R]. Beijing: Institute of Scientific and Technical Information of China, 2023.
2. Bommasani R, Hudson D A, Adeli E. et al. On the opportunities and risks of foundation models[J]. arXiv preprint arXiv: 2108.07258, 2021.
3. Goodfellow I., Pouget-Abadie J., Mirza, et, al. [J]. Generative Adversarial Networks. Arxiv Preprints. ArXiv: 1406.2661.
4. Mannuru N R, Shahriar S, Teel Z A, et al. Artificial intelligence in developing countries: The impact of generative artificial intelligence (AI) technologies for development[J]. Information Development, 2023: 02666669231200628.
5. Beijbom O.GPT-4 Architecture, Infrastructure, Training Dataset,Costs,Vision,MoE [EB/OL]. (2023-07).[2024-02-18]. https://www.nyckel.com/blog/discriminative-ai/.

Resilience of Underground Space System in Megacities: Connotation, Assessment Methods, Enhancement Strategies, and Prospects

Han Kaihang
PhD, Associate Researcher, and Deputy Director of the Underground Space Research Center, Underground Polis Academy of Shenzhen University (UPA)

> This is an excerpt from the author's speech at the 10th International Conference on Infrastructure Development of Underground Space.

1 Background

From the perspectives of population, area, and GDP, megacities (clusters) are highly important. After being affected by disasters, megacities not only impact the national economy but also bring about significant social consequences. Many countries and organizations worldwide are advocating for the promotion of building resilient cities. On April 10, 2020, President Xi Jinping highlighted the creation of resilient cities as a key focus for enhancing urbanization strategies during the seventh meeting of the Central Financial and Economic Affairs Commission. On March 12, 2021, "resilient cities" was included in the *Outline of the 14th Five-Year Plan for Economic and Social Development (2021–2025) and Long-Range Objectives through the Year 2035 of the People's Republic of China*. On October 16, 2022, President Xi Jinping stated in his report at the 20th National Congress of the Communist Party of China, "Guided by the principle that cities should be built by the people and for the people, we will improve urban planning, construction, and governance and move faster to change the development models of super-large cities and megacities. We will carry out urban renewal projects and improve urban infrastructure to build livable, resilient, and smart cities." On November 10, 2023, during an inspection of post-disaster recovery and reconstruction work in Beijing and Hebei Province, President Xi Jinping once again emphasized the construction of resilient cities, calling for a "comprehensive enhancement of disaster prevention, reduction, and relief capabilities". On December 1, 2023, during an inspection in Shanghai, President Xi Jinping first proposed a "comprehensive promotion of building resilient and safe cities", adding the word "safe" compared to the previous proposal of "building resilient cities". This adjustment carries profound and strategic implications.

One major background for building resilient cities is the shift in the development mode of megacities. In the past, urban development largely followed an extensive model, which often led to various urban issues such as traffic congestion, land resource shortages, urban flooding, and environmental pollution. To address the urban issues faced by megacities, developing underground spaces is one effective approach. On the one hand, it can increase the three-dimensional spatial carrying capacity of megacities, and on the other hand, it can increase green and blue spaces, enhancing the resilience and safety of the city while improving the quality of life for urban residents.

The three-dimensional space of megacities is a three-dimensional spatial form that integrates underground spaces, above-ground spaces, multi-layered surfaces, and vertical streets. Its characteristic is the emphasis on the development, coupling, and utilization of the vertical dimension of the city within a high population density and compact urban environment. Comprehensive disaster prevention and mitigation in the three-dimensional space of megacities, encompassing both above-ground and underground areas, is essential for ensuring the safe operation of these cities. However, three-dimensional urban spaces currently face challenges such as varying depths, insufficient coordination, and lack of resilience, leading to a weak comprehensive disaster prevention and mitigation capability in extreme situations. Taking the development and construction disturbances of deep underground spaces—engineering cataclysm and disaster as an example, the three-dimensional underground spaces, under the influence of multiple disasters, can easily trigger continuous and regional large-scale destruction from individual structures to structural groups. This may form collapse funnels, which can then affect the shallow or intermediate underground space systems, leading to the collapse of regional urban functions.

Ensuring the resilient development of deep underground spaces involves addressing several key scientific and technical issues. These include the mechanisms of damage evolution under underground structural disasters, resilience design methods, resilience assessment methods, research and development of materials and new structures, as well as techniques for rapidly repairing and enhancing the resilience of underground confined spaces and damaged underground concrete structures. In this context, for resilience assessment, both design and related technologies are quantifiable indicators. Therefore, it is a crucial component in the process of deep development.

2 Connotation of Resilience of Megacity Underground Space System

Megacities face various types of disasters, which can be broadly classified based on the duration of the disaster into impact-type and pressure-type disasters. Impact-type disasters have shorter duration, such as seismic events, explosions, and sudden geological disasters. Pressure-type disasters have longer duration, such as construction disturbances, gradual geological disasters, and slow-onset meteorological disasters. Furthermore, considering the time domain characteristics and predictability of different types of disasters, it is helpful to analyze the commonalities and differences in the resilience of the megacity underground space system from the perspective of disaster-adaptive resilience.

Experts and scholars from various disciplinary fields have conducted extensive research around the theme of "disaster-adaptive resilience", involving interdisciplinary integration in the field of underground spaces such as water resources, geoscience, energy science, materials, mechanics, environment, information, AI, and more. The purpose is to construct a typical urban underground space system that features "strong robustness, rich redundancy, quick recoverability, and intelligent adaptability". The ultimate goal is reflected in two key points: ① "resilience" corresponds to strong robustness, rich redundancy, and quick recoverability, and ② "intelligence" corresponds to intelligent adaptability (Fig. 1).

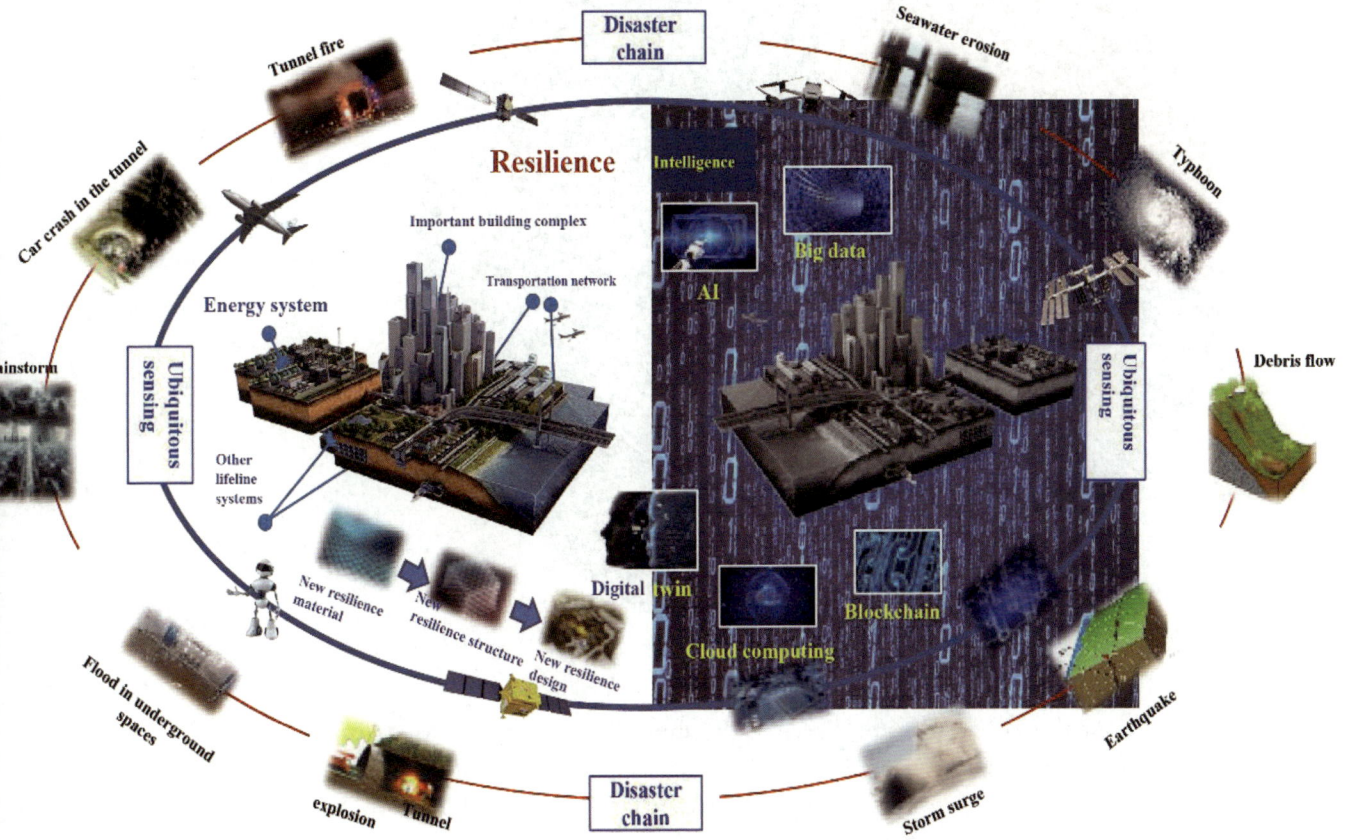

Fig. 1 Connotation of smart disaster-adaptive resilience of megacity underground space system

The research scope of the resilience of the megacity underground space system is vast. On the one hand, scholars from different disciplinary fields adopt significantly varied research scales, leading to a lack of comparability in assessment results. On the other hand, some scholars study the resilience of the megacity underground space system from a management perspective, while others approach it from civil engineering disciplines, resulting in significant differences in resilience assessment methods. Therefore, to thoroughly investigate the resilience of the megacity underground space system, it is necessary to conduct targeted research based on the emphasis of different disciplines. To this end, we propose the concept of "four features and three aspects" for the resilience of the megacity underground space system (Fig. 2), facilitating discussions on the adaptability of resilience assessments at different scales, dimensions, and measures for various types of disasters, as well as research into improving and innovating methods.

Fig. 2 "Four features and three aspects" of intelligence and resilience of megacity underground space system

Throughout the entire disaster process, the megacity underground space system exhibits a certain capacity to withstand the impacts of disasters (strong robustness), possesses the ability to prevent or block the further development of disaster chains after system damage (rich redundancy), can rapidly repair or enhance system functionality/structural performance post-disaster (quick recoverability), and can intelligently identify weak points in the system/structure during the disaster and invert perception data, achieving transparency in system structural deficiencies and/or geological defects to enhance the prevention and control objectives and control levels of system resilience (intelligent adaptability).

Regarding the dimension aspect, the resilience of the megacity underground space system can be categorized into six dimensions: organizational, economic, social, environmental, infrastructure, and community functions. Among these, the infrastructure dimension is a crucial support for the resilience of megacities, and due to the fact that underground infrastructure exists within geological and soil media, it adds complexity to research and increases the difficulty of enhancing resilience.

Regarding the scale aspect, we have proposed a method for scale division where the megacity underground space system can be divided into five scales: the first is the material scale; the second is the individual structural characteristic section scale; the third is the individual structure scale; the fourth is the regional underground engineering group scale; and the fifth is the urban underground engineering group network scale. The first four scales mainly emphasize the resilience of the structural entity, whether it be materials, components, or structural systems, while the fifth scale focuses more on functional resilience against disasters at the city level. After scale division, it becomes easier to study how small-scale cataclysms develop/couple with large-scale cataclysms, and it also facilitates the targeted establishment of resilience goals and enhancement strategies for each scale.

Regarding the measure aspect, from the perspective of the research progression of resilience: (1) The initial studies on engineering resilience often focus on the consequences (such as repair time, costs, and casualties) following disasters such as earthquakes and explosions (short time domain effects and unpredictable impacts) to conduct resilience assessment and optimize structural systems and enhance resilience based on the characteristics of ubiquitous damage and failure. (2) Subsequent research on the evolving resilience concept often focuses on the evolutionary patterns of the composite functions/performance of underground structural systems during disasters such as construction disturbance engineering disasters and slow-onset geological disasters (long time domain effects and predictable occurrence). Resilience assessments are frequently approached from the perspectives of resistance resilience, recovery resilience, and adaptive resilience. Based on these indicators and considering economic constraints, optimal strategies for enhancing resilience measures are formulated. (3) Unlike traditional engineering resilience and evolving resilience, to better reflect intelligent adaptability, we have explored and proposed the research concept of "intelligent resilience". For example, consider multiple instances of construction disturbances crossing existing structures. During the first crossing, the geological layers are not completely transparent, often represented by discrete borehole data. Defects in the geological layers and poor contact with existing underground structures and surrounding rock are not fully understood. Data collected during the first crossing are used for intelligent inversion to obtain more geological data, gradually achieving a process of "transparent geology". When crossing again, this enhances the resilience control level of the underground space structural system, reflecting its intelligent adaptability.

3 Assessment Methods and Enhancement Strategies for the Resilience of Megacity Underground Space System

I also provide a comprehensive review of resilience assessment methods and enhancement strategies.

(1) Material scale. This primarily emphasizes the research and development of new materials. In summary, our focus is on high toughness. For instance, high-fiber concrete materials, self-sensing concrete, and self-healing concrete. Self-healing concrete

includes microcapsules, bacteria, expansive aggregates, etc. Self-healing concrete is a material that will also be used in future underground spaces.

Research on materials used in underground structures provides the foundation for enhancing the resilience of the underground space system. Optimizing material ratios and introducing new types of materials are crucial methods for enhancing the disaster resistance of underground structures. However, at present, further attention is needed at this scale to focus on their adaptability and durability in underground environments, especially in deep underground conditions where coupled interactions are highly complex.

(2) Individual structural characteristic section scale. Research at this scale is relatively rich, often based on structural deformations, internal force indicators, and comprehensive new indicators. In the future, super-large diameter tunnels or super-large span underground frame structures will be planned and designed for urban deep underground spaces. The performance evolution characteristics of related structural systems in complex underground environments still require further research.

(3) Individual structure scale. This includes linear interval tunnel structures and nodal frame station structures, which often involve the mechanism of continuous collapse in underground structures, making it a significant research subject. Scale 3 serves as a complement and extension to Scale 2. The key aspect of resilience assessment at this scale is understanding the initiation, development, and cessation mechanisms of continuous collapse, as well as conducting range assessments.

(4) Regional underground engineering group scale. This aspect serves as a supplement and extension to the most critical section scale. Regarding research at this scale, Academician Chen Xiangsheng from Shenzhen University has led the National Natural Science Foundation Major Program "Basic Theory of Resilience of Megacity Deep Underground Spaces". The main research areas include (1) Mutual feedback effects and response mechanisms between underground spaces and regional geological environments; (2) Deterioration and recovery mechanisms of full-life performance of underground structures; (3) Disturbance cataclysm mechanisms and transmission mechanisms of underground space construction; (4) Proposing responsive resilience assessment theories by considering the coupled cataclysm mechanisms of rock-soil engineering systems.

(5) Urban underground engineering group network scale. Research at this scale is also very rich. It involves resilience assessments against disasters based on complex network considerations, including the spatial topological morphology of nodes and edges. However, there are three issues with these assessments: (1) The assessment scenarios focus on the impact of the external environment on the system, neglecting the inherent risks posed by the system itself and its internal structure throughout the entire disaster chain. (2) The assessment indicators emphasize technical performance indicators, overlooking social, economic, organizational, and institutional factors. The quantification methods lack scientific validation, and the determination of indicator weights is highly subjective. (3) The interconnections and interdependencies between

individual systems and other infrastructure are often ignored. The assessments do not delve into the interactions between systems under multiple disturbances.

4 Prospects

In the previous text, a brief overview of the five scales was provided. Now, let's outline six potentially crucial directions for the future.

The first aspect involves the significant impact of global climate change on cities. It focuses on analyzing and assessing slow-onset meteorological changes (sea-level rise and urbanization), extreme weather conditions (heavy rainfall and flooding, storm surges, and urbanization), and the occurrence of multiple disaster chains.

The second aspect involves assessment methods and resilience assessment theories for disasters and cataclysms under different scenarios. We expect to develop a multi-scale, multi-scenario, total-factor, and multi-time domain cataclysm analysis method and resilience assessment theory. It should consider economic constraints among different cities, integrate process resilience and state resilience for comprehensive dual-sided resilience assessment, and enhance the consideration of uncertainties in resilience assessment.

The third aspect involves innovative materials and collaborative structural systems. For new materials, the focus is on achieving high toughness, self-sensing capabilities, and self-repair properties. Concerning new components, they should possess functional, energy dissipation, and disaster chain-blocking functions. Regarding new structural systems, there is a need to establish a new cataclysm-resilient structural system with a multi-stage fusion mechanism.

The fourth aspect pertains to holistic and ubiquitous sensing, high-fidelity database construction, and the application of digital twin technology. This primarily emphasizes large-scale real-time ubiquitous self-sensing, which involves wireless pervasive sensing and large-area self-sensing materials for the creation of a real-time ubiquitous sensing system that collaboratively interacts with the external environment.

The fifth aspect focuses on autonomous decision-making and intelligent evolution based on AI technology. Data collection of the city is conducted based on AI technology, including data from digital twins. During the disaster chain process, each set of data collected by the city should undergo autonomous decision-making and evolution based on AI technology, enabling the city to adapt better to similar disasters in the future, much like how humans adapt.

The sixth aspect concerns the practical approach to the integrated platform of resilience and intelligence control. Currently, there is a pressing need to establish a multidimensional spatially collaborative "resilience-intelligence" control platform that enables real-time data exchange (Fig. 3). This platform consists of physical space, information space, and simulation space. Information collected in physical space is transferred to information space, which is crucial as it involves the inversion of terrain parameters and the fusion of massive data. Additionally, in the simulation space,

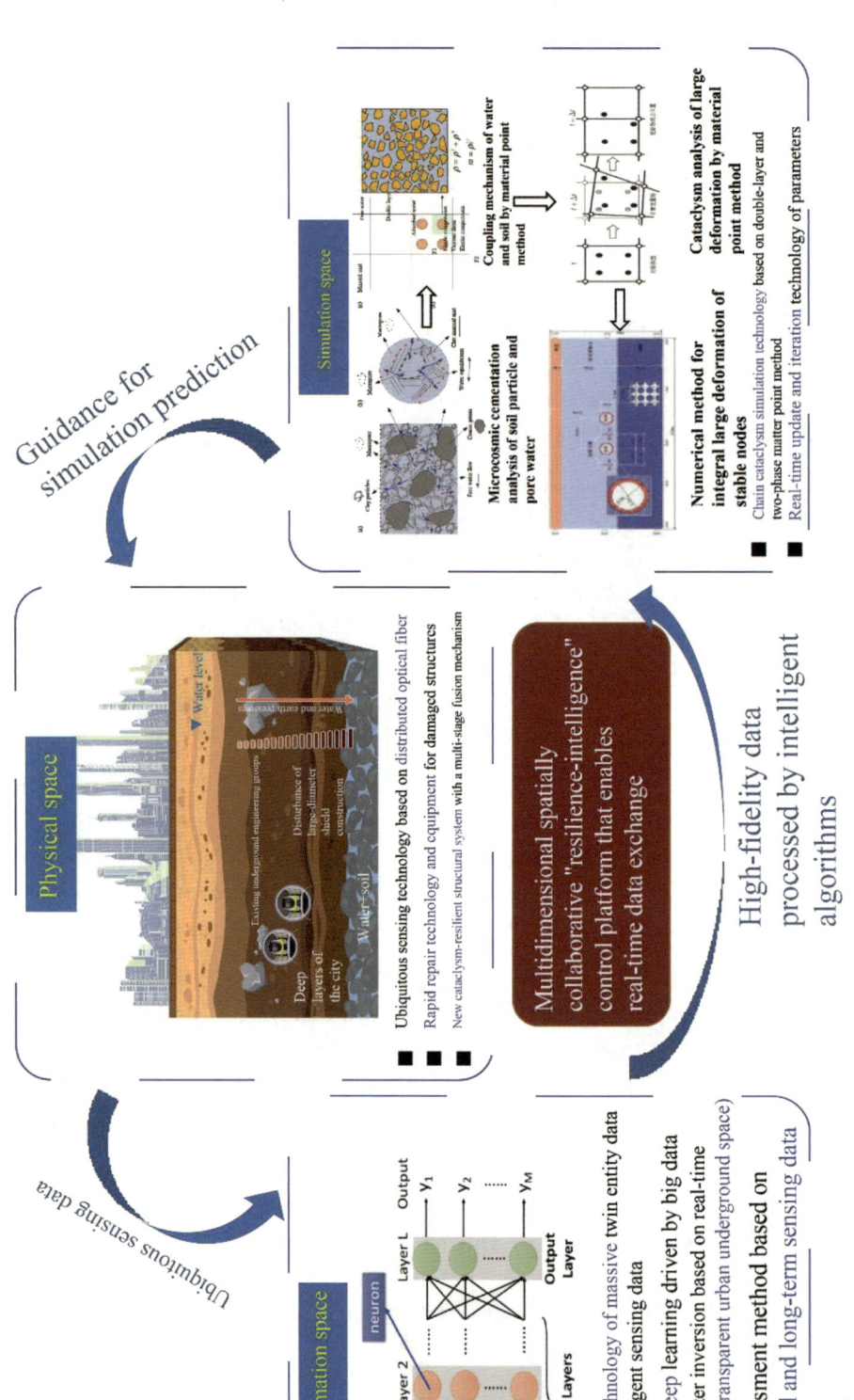

Fig. 3 PISMC practice path/practice method and system of "resilience-intelligence" control platform

efficient simulation technologies are used to predict potential evolution in the future. Through the continuous interaction among these three spaces, the ultimate goal of resilience control can be achieved.

In the preceding text, overviews and prospects were provided. For our team, we aim to propose a plan of UPA. This plan emphasizes research on multi-scale resilience assessment and visualization. Taking into account the application of AI technology and the trend of interdisciplinary development, it also requires collaborative innovation. Therefore, we have initially developed a framework. From the Guangdong-Hong Kong-Macao Greater Bay Area to Nanshan District in Shenzhen, and further to the Qianwan Area of Nanshan District, one of our research focuses is on digital twins, which includes real underground rail transit networks and potential underground logistics networks planned for construction in the future, fostering coordinated development. We also have data on surface landforms, terrain, architectural features, etc., which can be utilized for detailed simulations. The visually integrated platform showcasing the results of multi-scale, multi-scenario, total-factor, and multi-time domain cataclysm analysis methods and resilience assessments can achieve the following four functionalities: (1) Spatial topological distribution characteristics of high-precision underground structures (groups) and geological bodies (digital twins); (2) Real-time ubiquitous sensing system formed by wireless pervasive sensing and large-area self-sensing materials (multi-scale sensing system); (3) Adaptive methods for resilience assessment tailored to types of disasters (intelligent selection and assessment of cataclysm analysis and resilience assessment methods); (4) Autonomous decision-making and intelligent evolution based on AI technology (autonomous learning, intelligent adaptation, and immunity for experiences similar to past disasters).

5 Acknowledgment

The resilience of the urban underground space system is a broad research topic that involves extensive exploration. Throughout the research process, we have engaged in discussions with many professors and gained valuable insights, including Academician Chen Xiangsheng, Professor Su Dong, Professor Cui Hongzhi, Professor Bao Xiaohua, Professor Jin Yinfeng, Assistant Professor Lin Xingtao, and Assistant Professor Xiong Hao from Shenzhen University, as well as Professors Wang Enzhi (Tsinghua University), Chen Renpeng (Hunan University), Ding Wenqi (Tongji University), Zhang Dongmei (Tongji University), and Zhang Chengping (Beijing Jiaotong University). I would like to express my heartfelt gratitude to all of them. I also extend special thanks to the funding support from the Major Program of the National Natural Science Foundation, the Consulting Subject of the Chinese Academy of Engineering Major, and the Key R&D Program of the Ministry of Science and Technology, among a series of resilience-related programs. This concludes the content of this report. Thank you.

Chapter III

Shared Space and Infrastructure Construction

In-forest Venues, Eco-friendly Winter Olympics—Key technologies for the design, construction, operation and maintenance of the Winter Olympics snow venues under complex mountain conditions

Li Xinggang
Chief Expert of China Construction Techology Group Co., Ltd., National Survery and Design Master

This is an excerpt from the author's speech at the International Forum on Green and Low-carbon Building Technologies.

1 Foreword

The Olympic Winter Games Beijing 2022 is a significant milestone in China's history. The Yanqing competition area is located at the southern foothill of Xiaohaituo Mountain and includes major venue clusters such as the National Alpine Skiing Centre ("Xue Fei Yan", which literally means "a swallow flying in the snow"), the National Sliding Centre ("Xue You Long", meaning a giant dragon meandering amongst mountains), and the Yanqing Olympic Village. The construction scale covers an area of 800 hectares, with an elevation drop of 1,400 m, a maximum slope of snow tracks reaching 68%, a maximum wind speed of force 14 on the extended Beaufort scale, and a minimum temperature dropping below minus 40 degrees Celsius. It is situated near a national forest park and has a sensitive ecological environment.

Alpine skiing is hailed as the "jewel in the crown of the Winter Olympics", while the bobsleigh and luge events are referred to as the "Formula 1 of winter sports". These two events are the most challenging and most internationally watched in the Winter Olympics. However, they started late in our country and are facing a weak foundation. Due to their characteristics of being high-end and requiring customization", the construction of their venues is dominated by foreign technology, resulting in a lack of discourse power domestically. There is a complete void regarding them in our country. The Yanqing Olympic Village includes two star-rated hotels that operate after the Games, featuring a complex array of functional requirements. The Yanqing competition area faces five major challenges: complex terrain, harsh climate, fragile ecology, top-notch venues, and post-event utilization. The scale, measure, difficulty, and height differences of its construction projects far exceed those of conventional venues for the Winter Olympics.

In response to the unprecedented engineering challenges faced by the competition area, our team undertook the "High-tech Winter Olympics" key special project under the national key R&D plan under the 13th Five-Year Plan. We conducted research in various areas, including venue design and construction, ecological protection and restoration, full life cycle utilization, and new digital technologies. These efforts have supported the high-quality construction of the venue cluster in the Yanqing competition area, protected the ecological environment, created a positive Olympic legacy, and resulted in a series of achievements suitable for universal promotion.

2 Innovative Technologies and Achievements

Our team has established a methodological and technological system for the construction of in-forest venues that features the coexistence of sports and the ecological environment (Fig. 1), achieving breakthrough innovations in three key areas.

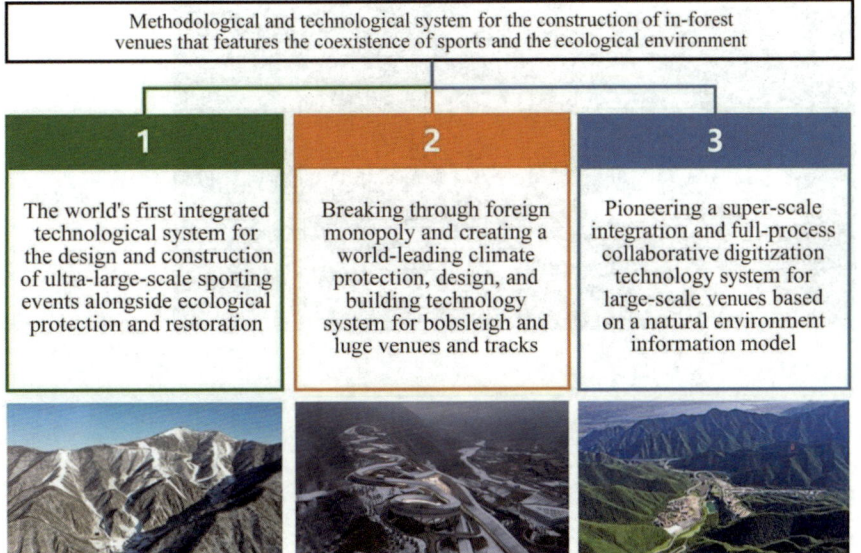

Fig. 1 Methodological and technological system for the construction of in-forest venues that features the coexistence of sports and the ecological environment

2.1 The world's first integrated technological system for the design and construction of ultra-large-scale sporting events alongside ecological protection and restoration

The National Alpine Skiing Centre features a uniquely designed high-altitude canyon track, with a maximum vertical drop of 925 m and a total length of 9.43 km. Competitors can reach speeds exceeding 150 km per hour. The venue is situated in a high, cold, and steep mountainous terrain with stringent requirements for flood prevention, fire safety, and earthquake resistance, and it must adapt to extreme weather conditions and a complex alpine environment. The Yanqing competition area is adjacent to the Songshan National Forest Park, boasting high biodiversity and attracting significant attention from both domestic and international communities. It is the largest venue in the Winter Olympics history to implement ecological protection and restoration efforts, with an elevation drop of over 1,400 m.

The research overcame the foreign monopoly on high-altitude ski venue design and addressed challenges posed by complex terrain and harsh climates. It pioneered the "context-adaptive, low-intervention, and reversible" technology (Fig. 2). Additionally, it tackled the global challenge of large mountain venue construction damaging the natural environment by establishing ecological protection and restoration techniques for environments with vertical drops exceeding 1,000 m (Fig. 3).

The results supported the establishment of China's first Winter Olympics-level alpine skiing venue, certified by the International Ski and Snowboard Federation (Fédération Internationale de Ski et du Snowboard, FIS) as world-leading. The Yanqing competition area is renowned as the most ecologically distinctive venue of

Fig. 2 Application effect of the "context-adaptive, low-intervention, and reversible" technology

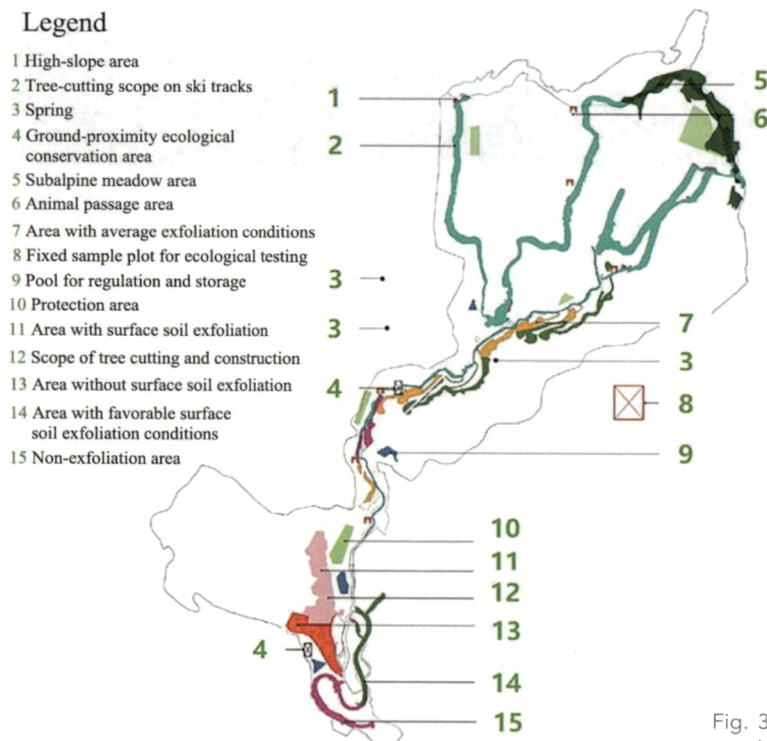

Fig. 3 Ecological protection and restoration engineering distribution map

the Winter Olympics, receiving significant attention and high praise from the international community.

2.2 Breaking through foreign monopoly and creating a world-leading climate protection, design, and building technology system for bobsleigh and luge venues and tracks

The National Sliding Centre features the 17th bobsleigh and luge track in the world and the first in China. The track's traditional construction technology has long been monopolized by a few institutions, such as Germany's Deyle, with no domestic venue design specifications, engineering standards, or materials technology and construction methods in place. The selection of the bobsleigh and luge venues and tracks is closely related to the conditions of the mountain chosen. Due to the inability to find suitable construction sites on the northern slopes within the competition area, extensive discussions led to the conclusion that the Yanqing track would become the only southern slope track and high-intensity seismic-resistant track in the world. There is a lack of relevant experience and standards internationally.

The research has solved the challenge of the world's only southern slope track, pioneering the "terrain and climate protection system" for tracks across the globe (Fig. 4), which protects over 98% of tracks from solar radiation and other climatic influences. The research has also tackled the challenge of building tracks with the highest seismic precautionary intensity (8 degrees, with a designed basic acceleration magnitude amid an earthquake of 0.30 g) and the utmost precision (millimeter-level). It has pioneered the design and integrated molding technology of three-dimensional, irregularly-shaped, curved-surface, and ultra-long thin-shell tracks (Fig. 5), breaking the foreign monopoly and raising international standards for track design.

The National Sliding Centre, supported by these achievements, has been certified and evaluated by the International Bobsleigh and Skeleton Federation (IBSF) as the best sliding center in the world. It has overcome the conventional limitations of venue site selection and paved the way for a new model for the future construction of international bobsleigh and luge venues.

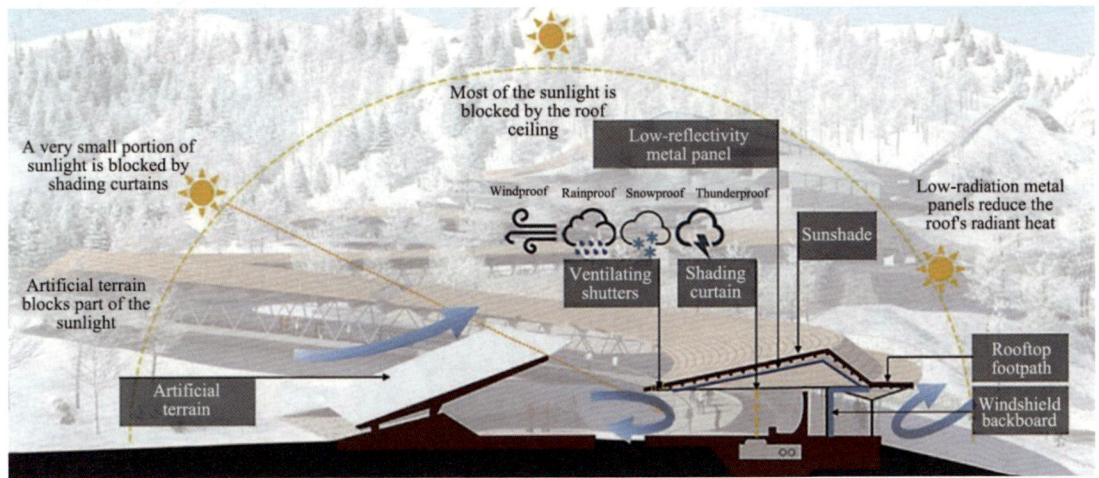

Fig. 4 "Terrain and climate protection system" for tracks

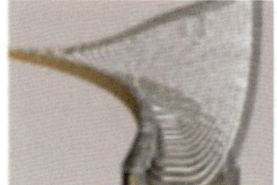

Fig. 5 Integrated forming of ultra-long thin-shell tracks

2.3 Pioneering a super-scale integration and full-process collaborative digitization technology system for large-scale venues based on a natural environment information model

The Yanqing competition area stands as a Winter Olympics competition area with the most intensively constructed venues and infrastructure. The super-scale natural mountainous terrain precisely connects and integrates with its digital design and construction information such as tracks and venues, setting a precedent that has never been seen before. The design, construction, operation, and maintenance processes of alpine and valley ski tracks, uniquely shaped, curved-surface tracks, and super-large, elongated in-mountain venues require an exceptionally high level of information transmission, which traditional technology cannot support.

We have developed a super-scale integrated digital design and construction technology for major venues, based on a natural environmental information model (Fig. 6). This ensures the accuracy, safety, and ecological harmony of constructing ultra-large venues in complex mountainous conditions. We have developed a "BIM+" information collaboration technology based on multi-scenario transitions for design, construction, operation, and maintenance (Fig. 7), which enables successive information transmission throughout the entire construction process of ultra-large inmountain venues.

Fig. 6 Super-scale integration of large-scale venues based on a natural environment information model

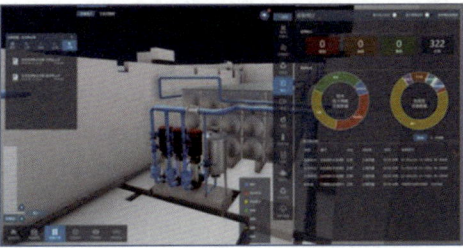

Fig. 7 A comprehensive smart operation and maintenance management platform for and after competition time featuring functions such as energy regulation and traffic management for complex in-mountain venues

The results supported the completion of the Yanqing competition area venue cluster within an extremely tight schedule, helping achieve the goal of constructing ultra-large-scale "Eco-friendly Winter Olympics" venues and facilitating all-scene operations throughout the design/construction phase and during/after event stages.

3 Achievement Promotion and Benefits

The research outcomes of this project are applied to multi-type engineering construction and industry digital transformation, such as the construction and ecological protection of large-scale sports event venues and large-scale mountainous environmental engineering projects, as well as Milan's venues for the 2026 Winter Olympics, public sports and entertainment facilities, and unconventional structural civil engineering, resulting in significant environmental and social benefits.

3.1 Environmental benefits

A model competition area for a green Olympics that embodies the symbiosis of sports and ecology has been established, becoming a landmark project for in-mountain venues and an eco-friendly Winter Olympics. The ecological restoration of the competition area covers 204 hectares, with 195 hectares dedicated to the traumatic restoration of bare mountains. Within the competition area, 11,027 shrub and herbaceous plants were transplanted in situ or from nearby, along with 24,272 trees transplanted from other locations. An in-situ restoration of subalpine meadows covers 2,400 m^2, along with the protection of a seed bank of 400,000 m^3 (Fig. 8).

Fig. 8 A model competition area for a green Olympics that embodies the symbiosis of sports and ecology

A model project for a green Winter Olympics has been established. All venues in the Yanqing competition area have received a three-star "green" certification, and the in-mountain press center has been established as a near-zero energy consumption demonstration site. The competition area exceeded its sustainability commitment to ensure that "all newly constructed venues meet the three-star standard for green building evaluation".

A new pathway for environmental sustainability in competition area construction has been built. During the event, 100% green electricity was used, and on-site management processed 310,000 m³ of construction gravel. An unpowered chute technology was utilized for 100,000 m³ of construction muck, achieving zero energy consumption. The main building structure was installed with zero air pollution and zero risk of fire or explosion. Comprehensive water resource management resulted in a 30% reduction in annual water consumption, while there was zero discharge of melt snow-containing sewage from the snow trails. Additionally, the National Sliding Centre employed a cooling-heating combined system, which reduced annual carbon emissions by approximately 160,000 kg.

3.2 Social benefits

The competition area was built from scratch to fill a gap and meet the highest requirements for hosting the Winter Olympics, making a significant contribution to the successful hosting of the Olympic Winter Games Beijing 2022. In just five years, the world's best sliding center and a leading alpine skiing venue were built from nothing, achieving "the most challenging competition area for the Winter Olympics". On January 18, 2021, Xi Jinping, the General Secretary of the Communist Party of China, praised the team and builders of the Yanqing competition area, stating, "China has built the best snow sports venues in the world, and you, construction personnel have made historic contributions." He also said, "The builders of the competition area are remarkable, and every Chinese person is remarkable."

Support was offered to implement the *Olympic Agenda 2020* in the most challenging competition area of the Winter Olympics throughout the process, showcasing China's engineering prowess and cultural confidence to the world through the demonstration of application results in a high-tech Winter Olympics. Juan Antonio Samaranch Jr, Chairman of the IOC (International Olympic Committee) Coordination Commission for Beijing 2022, lauded the National Alpine Skiing Centre as a perfect venue for top-level downhill competitions. Ivo Ferriani, President of IBSF, remarked that the National Sliding Centre was one of the exemplary representations of China showcasing its new image to the future and the world since 2008.

Underground Space and Urban Resilience

Zhou Yingxin
Fellow, Academy of Engineering, Singapore

> This is an excerpt from the author's speech at the 10th International Conference on Infrastructure Development of Underground Space.

1 The Story of Water

Singapore is a city-state with extremely limited land resources. With a growing population and increasing urbanization, effectively using these limited land resources has been a significant challenge. However, when Singapore became independent in 1965, a more pressing challenge was managing its water supply and flooding. From survival to water sustainability and resilience, Singapore's story of water is a good case study of long-term planning, and systematic implementation and management, and making use of underground space as part of the water system. Singapore's achievements offer valuable insights for the global community.

The Public Utilities Board (PUB) of Singapore has approached the issue of water sustainability and resilience by treating the entire water loop as a system to carry out complete planning, development, and management of water resources. This includes the sourcing, collection, purification, and supply of drinking water, wastewater treatment and its conversion into new water, and the collection and drainage of rainwater.

To date, Singapore has 17 reservoirs across the island, making it the world's largest urban catchment area despite her limited land resources. The long-term goal is to increase the catchment area from the current two-thirds to 90 percent of the land area. In terms of underground space, Singapore's deep tunnel sewerage system (DTSS) has revolutionized the management of urban catchments, enabling the adoption of two completely separate systems for sewage and rainwater (Fig. 1). This separation ensures that rainwater collection remains unpolluted. As a further example of making use of the underground space, Singapore's fourth seawater desalination plant—Keppel Marina East Desalination Plant was built underground (Fig. 2). The plant is also integrated with the Park Connector Network (PCN) and with the aboveground accessible to the public. It is also capable of purifying both fresh water and seawater.

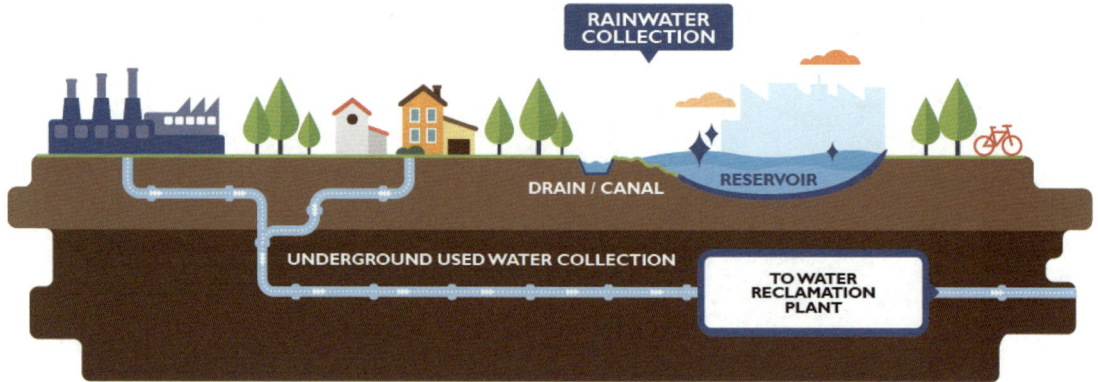

Fig. 1　The Deep Tunnel Sewage System of Singapore

Fig. 2　Keppel Marina East Desalination Plant connecting parkland

Since 1965, Singapore has made significant achievements in managing water resources. With annual precipitations exceeding 2,000 mm, and its relatively flat terrain and many low-lying areas, Singapore frequently experienced widespread flooding in its early days. Flood-prone areas in Singapore have been reduced from 3,178 hectares in 1970 to 40 hectares by 2013, despite extensive urban development (Fig. 3). This number was further decreased to 27 hectares by 2022. In 2016, Singapore was ranked 22nd in water sustainability among 50 cities from 31 countries by Arcadia. Singapore's journey from a state of severe water scarcity and frequent flooding to its current achievements in water governance is highly commendable. It clearly demonstrates that with proper planning and management and proper use of underground space, urban development does not inherently lead to "urban maladies".

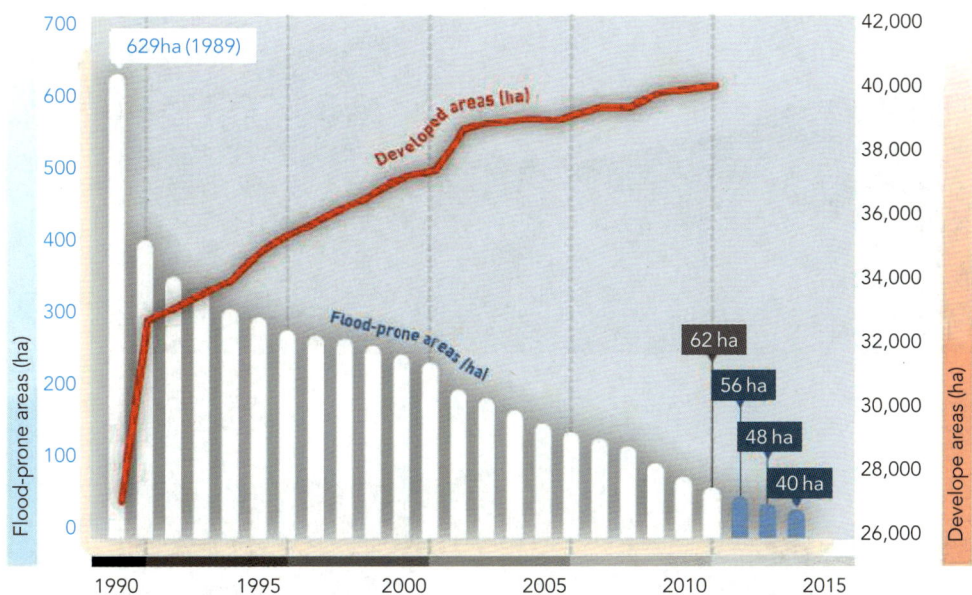

Fig. 3 Decreasing flood-prone area in Singapore

2 Approaches to Climate Change

Singapore's approaches to climate change mainly include four aspects: First, protecting the coastline by raising the minimum level for land reclamation by 1 meter from the original requirement of 1.25 m above the highest recorded tide level set in 1991. Second, the building and infrastructure platform level is required to be 4.0 m above the Singapore Height Datum for projects along the southern coast, and 4.5 m above the Singapore Height Datum for projects along the northern coast. Third, addressing flood risks by adapting its infrastructure to the longer- term effects of rising sea level and rainfall intensity, with the aim of effectively responding to the challenges posed by extreme weather. Fourth, managing water resources to provide a robust and diversified water supply for Singapore through the Four National Taps, namely local catchment water, imported water, NEWater, and desalinated water, ensuring sufficient water resources under all situations.

Regarding water resources and future flood control management, Singapore has implemented a range of planning initiatives.

Singapore plans to implement 100 projects in her Active, Beautiful, Clean Waters (ABC Waters) programme, varying in scale and content. Fig. 4 shows one of the flagship ABC Waters projects at Ang Mo Kio, where a traditional concrete drainage channel has been transformed into a beautiful and vegetated area, leading to a 40% increase in flood discharge capacity and a 30% increase in biological species.

In response to climate change, Singapore has studied various options for long-term plans for resilient cities. Among these is an underground drainage and reservoir sys-

Fig. 4 Bishan Park ABC Water Project with canal reconstruction

tem (UDRS) across the island to facilitate drainage, flood control, water storage, and pumped hydro energy storage (Fig. 5). By harvesting storm water, the underground reservoir greatly reduces the carbon footprint compared to seawater desalination and NEWater while achieving land savings, enhanced water security, and reduced evaporation. Another significant plan is to develop a reclaimed long island along the eastern coast to tackle rising sea levels in the future. This plan, if implemented, is set to offer various benefits, including coastline protection, land space creation, rainwater harvesting, and flood prevention (Fig. 6).

With the story of water in Singapore as the background, I will discuss the topic of urban resilience. What is urban resilience? Urban resilience is the capacity of city systems, businesses, institutions, communities, and individuals to survive, adapt, and grow, no matter what chronic stresses and acute shocks they experience. Singapore's water resource problem poses long-term pressure on it. The optimal approach is to eliminate or minimize these risks during the planning and design stages, ensuring urban systems have the capacity to survive, adapt, and grow.

In recent years, climate change has intensified, manifesting in rising temperatures and droughts, rising sea levels, and frequent extreme weathers. All these have cul-

Going underground

PUB is exploring using underground space to protect Singapore's inland and coastal areas from flooding. This comes amid the growing threats of rising sea levels with climate change and more intense rainfall.

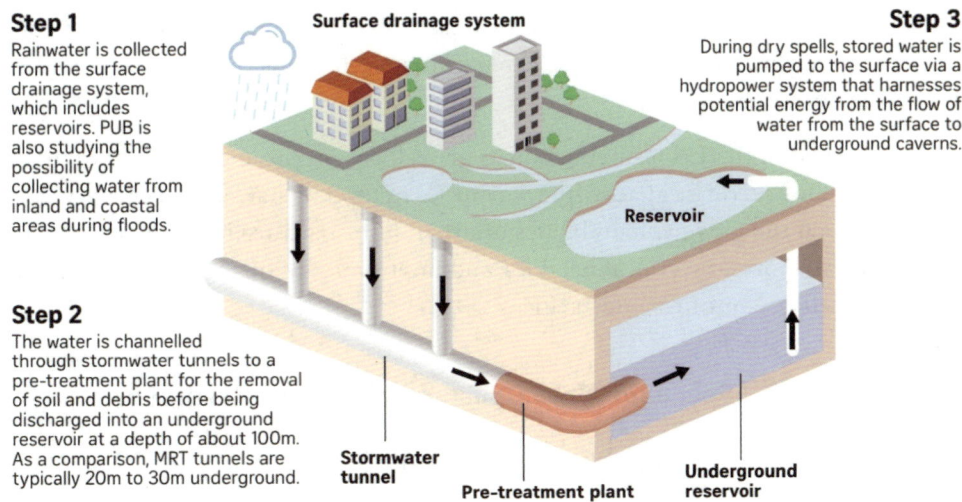

Step 1
Rainwater is collected from the surface drainage system, which includes reservoirs. PUB is also studying the possibility of collecting water from inland and coastal areas during floods.

Step 2
The water is channelled through stormwater tunnels to a pre-treatment plant for the removal of soil and debris before being discharged into an underground reservoir at a depth of about 100m. As a comparison, MRT tunnels are typically 20m to 30m underground.

Step 3
During dry spells, stored water is pumped to the surface via a hydropower system that harnesses potential energy from the flow of water from the surface to underground caverns.

Fig. 5 The Underground Drainage and Reservoir System

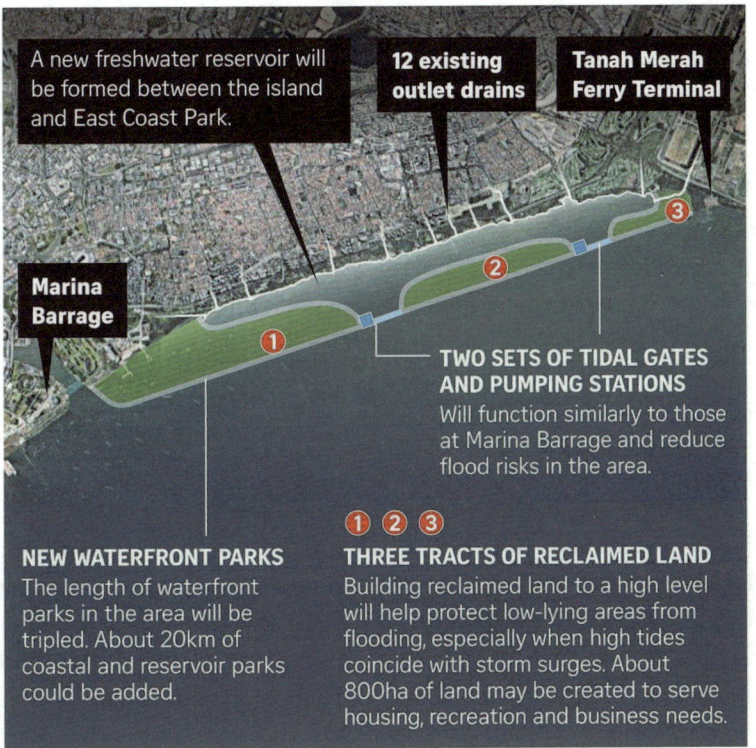

Fig. 6 The Long Island

Chapter III Shared Space and Infrastructure Construction

minated in a climate crisis. In 2022, the Yangtze River in Wuhan was parched when the city suffered a severe drought. During the drought, Poyang Lake's area shrank by 75%. The Zhengzhou flood in 2021 resulted in heavy casualties and substantial economic losses. The United States Geological Survey (Holmes & Dinicola, 2010), in an article discussing flood control, stated, "We have had two 100-year floods in 15 years!" Due to climate change, the historical data used in flood control planning and design have become obsolete because climate change shortens the flood cycle and increases the peak rainfalls.

If the 911 event in the US brought about a great focus on protection of critical infrastructure against terrorist attacks, the war in Ukraine that started in February 2022 clearly exposed the grave vulnerabilities of urban infrastructure in a military conflict. All these underscores the critical need for and importance of better protection of critical infrastructures for our modern cities.

3 Underground Space for Urban Sustainability and Resilience

If the sky falls, where will we go? Go underground!

Underground space plays crucial roles in urban resilience and sustainability. The key benefits include:

(1) Land savings and compact cities: Underground space is a key enabler of compact cities. The utilization of underground space helps save valuable surface land resources. By relocating infrastructure and public facilities underground, cities can leave more surface space for greening and public use, thereby enhancing the quality of urban life.

(2) Energy savings and reduced carbon emissions: Underground facilities typically exhibit high energy efficiency, leading to reduced energy use and carbon emissions. The constant temperature of underground space offers a substantial benefit in terms of energy consumption, contributing to the goal of creating a low-carbon city.

(3) Safety and protection: Underground space offers excellent protection against external attacks and natural disasters. For example, underground buildings can effectively withstand blasts, fires, and extreme weather, offering a safe shelter.

The protection and safety in underground space are reflected in three key aspects. First, underground space offers protection against external hazards and threats, including superior protection against external weapons or vehicle bombs, significant operational advantages (difficult to locate, identify, hit, and assess damage), resistance to external fire, wind, and accidental blasting damage, excellent concealment and camouflage, and enhanced physical security (easy to control access). Second, underground space protects the external environment from potential accidents of stored hazardous materials (including explosives, oil, and hazardous materials), minimizing external effects in case of accidents. Third, it is a cheaper option for protection. Above-ground buildings are more susceptible to radiation exposure, resulting in increased damage and casualties. Conversely, underground space offers significant advantages in this regard. It provides higher levels of protection at a lower cost compared to above-ground buildings.

Many critical infrastructures leverage the advantages of underground space protection. These include transport systems & utilities, dual-purpose bomb shelters, telecommunications, civil defense control centers, storage of clean water/food, strategic oil reserve and gas storage, national archives, and power stations.

For example, the main venue for the 1994 Winter Olympics held in Norway was located in the world's largest rock cavern with a span of 61 meters. This cavern facility can function as a stadium or a concert hall that seats 5,000 people and serves as a wartime bomb shelter (Fig. 7). This design not only maximizes the utilization of underground space but also demonstrates its advantages in multi-functional use and protection.

Fig. 7   Underground stadium in Norway (Hermansen, 2006)

Chapter III Shared Space and Infrastructure Construction

In the vast majority of cases when an earthquake occurs, above-ground facilities suffer severe damage, while underground facilities experience relatively minimal damage. During the 2011 Earthquake in Sendai, Japan, the underground sections of subway and railway networks suffered only minor damage, while most above-ground natural gas facilities near the seaside were destroyed. Underground LNG tanks remained safe, while above-ground power plants were destroyed. Underground electric transmission lines were only damaged at 14 locations and the water piping network and high-pressure gas pipes experienced minor damage.

There were four nuclear power accidents from 1969 to 2021, and the only one without any casualties or damages occurred at an underground nuclear power plant in Switzerland. Lessons from the Fukushima nuclear accident show that underground caverns provide the best protection against external threats or hazards and only a deep cavern might limit radioactive emissions in the atmosphere, minimizing the impact on the external environment.

Urban infrastructure is a highly complex network system characterized by interdependencies among various systems. Planning and development of urban infrastructure therefore requires a systems approach. It is essential to comprehensively consider the interconnected relationships among various infrastructures to optimize urban resilience. Accelerating climate change and geopolitical conflicts have exposed the vulnerabilities of urban infrastructure. Moreover, previous climate assumptions are outdated, and historical data is no longer applicable to urban planning for current and future climatic conditions. Therefore, urban planning and design should be based on the latest climate data to ensure that cities can adapt to new challenges such as extreme weather and rising sea levels.

Underground space offers unique advantages in urban resilience and sustainability. Key benefits include land savings, compact urban layout, energy savings and reduced carbon emissions, and safety and protection. By systematically planning and maximizing the use of underground space, we can more effectively address climate change and other urban challenges, thereby promoting urban sustainability and resilience.

References

1. Hermansen, T. "Strategic Infrastructure, defence, combined purposes". in Sustainable Underground Concepts[J]. Norwegian Tunnelling Society, 2006, 15.
2. Robert R. Holmes, R.R. and K. Dinicola (2010). "100-Year Flood—It's All About Chance." U.S. Geological Survey. General Information Product 106.
3. Public Utilities Board (PUB), https://www.pub.gov.sg.
4. The Straits Times, 2023. PUB explores underground space to protect Singapore against rising sea levels. 03/01/2023.

Cases and Experience of Urban Near-Zero Carbon Community Construction in China

Zhang Yalong
President of Science-Innovation Institute of Sustainable Development, Longgang District, Shenzhen

This is an excerpt from the author's speech at the 2023 World Cities Day 'Urban Environment' Forum.

In July 2023, the global temperature hit a new high. UN Secretary-General António Guterres declared, "The era of global warming has ended and the era of global boiling has arrived. Extreme weather is nothing less than a warning sign of a dire future for humanity". Compared with Europe and the United States, China faces greater challenges in achieving carbon neutrality. In terms of total emissions, China's total carbon emissions are more than twice that of the United States and over three times that of the European Union (EU). Consequently, the reduction in carbon emissions required for China to achieve carbon neutrality is significantly higher than that of other economies. In terms of the development stage, Europe and the United States have successfully decoupled economic development from carbon emissions. China is still experiencing rapid industrialization and urbanization, accompanied by economic growth and peak carbon dioxide emissions. It is crucial to address the contradiction between balancing carbon emissions with social and economic development. In terms of decarbonization time, the period from peak carbon dioxide emissions to carbon neutrality in China is much shorter compared to that in the United States and the EU. However, based on the long-term goal of global sustainable development, achieving carbon neutrality is imperative.

Zero carbon is the future direction for urban renewal and development while serving as the cornerstone for sustainable urban development. Meanwhile, carbon neutrality is a crucial metric for quantifying sustainable development achievements within cities. Under the current conditions, the essence of a zero-carbon city centers on "implementing demonstration projects in near-zero carbon emission areas". This concept was initially proposed in the *CPC Central Committee's Proposal for Formulating the 13th Five-Year Plan for National Economic and Social Development* in March 2015. Under the national vision of achieving peak carbon dioxide emissions and carbon neutrality, it is urgent for China to establish near-zero carbon emission demonstration zones across six pilot categories: regions, parks, communities, campuses, buildings, and enterprises. Building on the foundation of existing low-carbon pilot projects, these demonstration zones aim to support China's dual carbon goals of peaking carbon emissions by 2030 and reaching carbon neutrality by 2060.

By analyzing every cell, unit, and scenario within a city in the context of zero-carbon development, we can find that communities, serving as the cells of cities, form the foundation for the zero-carbon city construction. However, as traditional community operations have expanded in scale, the community construction within a zero-carbon city focuses on transforming and upgrading these traditional communities. To achieve carbon neutrality and digitalization in the next 30 years, Cloud Carbon is the most cost-effective, efficient, and balanced approach in terms of efficiency, cost, and resources. Located on the north side of Gaoqiao Village in Shenzhen International Low Carbon City, Xinqiao Shiju Near-zero Carbon Community introduces an innovative concept in zero carbon community construction. This approach emphasizes a multi-dimensional interaction among zero carbon cells (residents), zero carbon units (families), and zero carbon scenarios (communities). The community integrates and applies over 100 green low-carbon technologies, with a focus on fields regarding cloud carbon smart platforms, clean energy, green commuting, and green buildings, basically achieving near-zero carbon emissions (Fig. 1).

Fig. 1   Xinqiao Shiju Near-zero Carbon Community

Residents entering the community can log in by scanning the QR code to connect with the Community Carbon Smart Management Platform. Residents and visitors can establish personal carbon centers using big data and artificial intelligence (AI), offering clear insights into their carbon footprint and carbon emissions. Through centralized carbon management for community residents and visitors, green commuting and living habits can be fostered, enabling individual residents to achieve near-zero carbon emissions. It is estimated that the basic carbon emissions of the above-mentioned community amount to approximately 630 tons per year. Through the application of various energy-saving and carbon reduction equipment and technologies, these emissions can potentially be lowered by about 580 tons annually. The remaining 50 tons of carbon emissions will be managed by establishing a carbon account for community residents and visitors. Residents can earn carbon points in their carbon accounts by engaging in green behaviors. These points can be used to exchange for commodities in the Carbon Mall or sold on the carbon trading platform, encouraging residents to adopt a zero-carbon lifestyle (Fig. 2).

Fig. 2 Xinqiao Shiju Cloud Carbon Platform

In the process of building a near-zero carbon community, our focus is also changing. We focused more on technological innovation in the early stage. In the middle stage, our emphasis shifted to model innovation, and in the later stage, we prioritized operational innovation. A successful community should prioritize fostering residents' behaviors as the driving force, rather than relying solely on technological transformation. Once technological transformation becomes the main force, it has been found that rigid investments or mandatory carbon reduction capacity should be no less than RMB 10 million. We have devoted a lot of time and energy to scientifically defining and guiding resident behaviors, transforming these behaviors into data. This data is then converted into carbon assets, represented as carbon points, which are subsequently traded on the exchange. Communities can easily reduce carbon emissions if they are willing to invest financially. However, at the city and national levels, capital considerations become crucial. Therefore, we must prioritize the transformation into green operations to achieve carbon neutrality, allowing residents to experience a life scenario rather than a world of technology (Fig. 3).

Therefore, to achieve carbon neutrality and digitalization in the next 30 years, Cloud Carbon is the most cost-effective, efficient, and balanced approach in terms of effi-

Fig. 3 Xinqiao Shiju real scene picture

ciency, cost, and resources. Technology is a double-edged sword, so evaluating technology and resources requires a systematic and balanced approach. Achieving digital urban carbon neutrality requires continuous innovation in three dimensions: model, operation, and technology. This involves developing net-zero carbon smart buildings and promoting AI-enabled carbon data analysis. Additionally, it is imperative to mobilize more social forces and resources to collaborate in attaining the ultimate goal of carbon peaking and carbon neutrality, paving the way for a zero-carbon future.

The foundation of today's near-zero carbon communities is built on data and operations. It is essential to validate real data through operations to assess whether the community's low-carbon capabilities are sustainable. We should prioritize sustainability over focusing solely on rapid or innovative development. We hope to ultimately integrate our carbon platform into the existing smart city infrastructure, enhancing efforts in carbon reduction and digitization to support the formation of carbon assets, which can then be converted into carbon finance in the trading market. This process involves significant capital and technological investments. Only through this can we secure substantial funds guarantee and achieve results that best align with our technologies.

Human beings play a vital role in achieving "carbon neutrality" for cities and communities. We hope that everyone will engage more actively in the future development of near-zero carbon communities by evolving their concepts and behaviors, and embracing their responsibilities. A truly low-carbon future can be achieved when everyone recognizes that reducing carbon emissions is both a personal and generational duty.

Achieving the "dual carbon" goal requires not just technological progress but also innovative concepts. We encourage everyone to become a practitioner and communicator of a low carbon lifestyle. Thank you!

Reshaping Functions and Reviving Character
—Practices and Explorations in Urban Renewal and Cultural Root Preservation in Shanghai

Liu Qianwei[*] Chen Zhuo[**]

[*] Chief Engineer of the Shanghai Municipal Commission of Housing, Urban-Rural Development and Management

[**] Deputy Director of Urban Renewal Department of Shanghai Municipal Commission of Housing Urban Rural Development and Management

This is an excerpt from the author's speech at the Inheriting Historical Context & Building Sci-Tech New City Forum.

The vitality of a city lies in its continuous renewal and the persistent energy it generates, and renewal is an enduring state and a constant theme in urban development. The decision made at the 20th National Congress of the Communist Party of China to "implement the action plan for urban renewal" has necessitated urban renewal for high-quality urban development under the laws of urban development.

Shanghai is famous for its history and culture, and its successive CPC municipal committees and governments have consistently prioritized the protection of historic buildings and historical character, with a repeated emphasis on the significant responsibility of the municipal government to protect historical character and historic buildings. When implementing the action plan for urban renewal, Shanghai aims to advance the high-standard protection, high-quality utilization, and high-level preservation of its cultural heritage and historical character and create a "Shanghai model" for the protection and renewal of historical character in the context of Chinese-style modernization.

1 Case 1: Old Housing Renovation Project in Futian Village, Zhangjiazhai, Jing'an District

The lane houses in Shanghai are quintessential Shanghai-style architecture, seamlessly blending the essence of Chinese and Western residential cultures, while also serving as living spaces for millions. In 1988, during the annual exchange visits between Shanghai and its sister city Rotterdam, urban old housing transformation was included in a memorandum of cooperation between the two cities. In 1992, Futian Village in the Zhangjiazhai Subdistrict of Jing'an District (Fig. 1 and Fig. 2), located in the central area of Shanghai, was chosen as a pilot project for old housing transformation under the friendly cooperation between China and the Netherlands. New design concepts were introduced, and while ensuring the thorough protection of the original architectural character, volume, layout, and structural system, internal

Fig. 1 Futian Village before Transformation

transformation and renewal were made following the Dutch housing standards at that time, using new materials and equipment from the Netherlands to improve the functional quality of the buildings. Upon completion of the transformation, each household had its private kitchen and bathroom, with a living space of over 8 square meters per capita, meeting the standards set for a moderately prosperous society in Shanghai at that time.

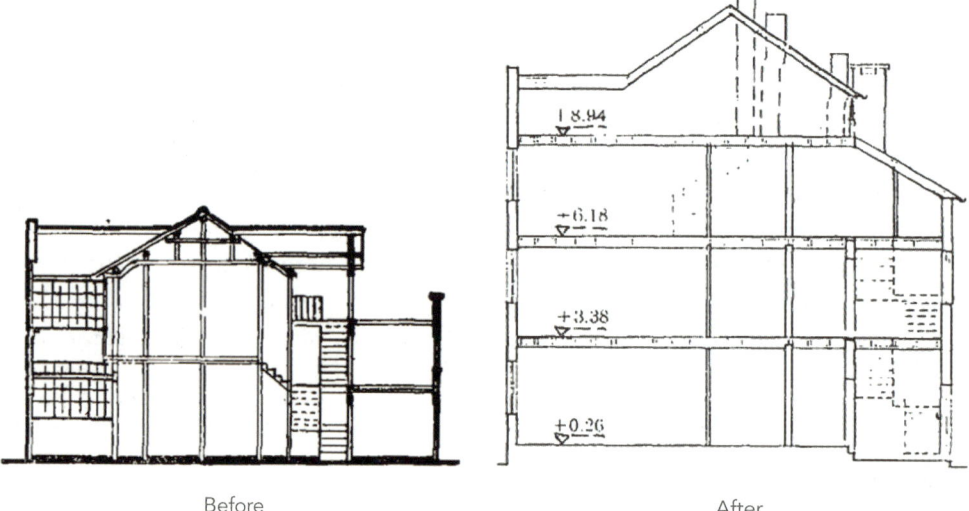

Before

After

Fig. 2 Before and After section of Futian village residential Transformation

Although the transformation standards for Futian Village may seem relatively low by today's benchmarks, exploratory projects such as Futian Village and Penglai Road Lane 303 over three decades ago significantly advanced the process of old housing transformation in Shanghai, laying a solid foundation for implementing the subsequent old housing transformation plans. Shanghai has come to understand that tackling urban housing issues is not merely a matter of demolition and reconstruction but involves essential value-based decision-making; there are no one-size-fits-all solutions;

and ongoing efforts are necessary to explore multiple avenues for meeting residential needs. While the previous transformation, expansion, and utilization of old buildings might not have been primarily driven by the need for protection and preservation, they raised the awareness of the value and feasibility of protecting and utilizing modern architecture. The residential lane houses represent the essence of the city's image, embodying irreplaceable historical and cultural significance.

2 Case 2: Huangpu District Waitanyuan Project (Phase I)

In 2003, the *Regulations on the Protection of Historical and Cultural Landscapes and Excellent Historic Buildings in Shanghai* were enacted, with the CPC municipal committee and municipal government emphasizing the establishment of "the strictest protection system". This made Shanghai one of the first cities in China to focus on the collective protection of modern architecture and historical and cultural landscapes. The city designated 15 specific areas, including Waitanyuan, Sinan Road, and Jianye Lane, as pilot projects for protection and renovation. The initiative aimed to "enhance distinctive features, optimize spaces, beautify the environment, and implement a strict protection system during the renovation process". Among these projects, the Huangpu District Waitanyuan Project (Fig. 3) focused on preserving the original appearance of 14 historic buildings and restoring them to their former glory, carrying out transformation, development, and operations by adjusting the usage and commercial operations of these buildings.

Fig. 3 Waitanyuan along the Suzhou Creek

During this phase, the concept of collective protective renovation and transformation was proposed, complementing the protection of individual buildings, and a categorized preservation and protection strategy encompassing "demolition, transformation, and preservation" was implemented, which effectively avoided large-scale demolition and reconstruction while preventing a rigid form of protection. The projects also engaged social forces in the protection efforts, exploring methods to "utilize market mechanisms, encourage corporate participation, and leverage government policy support".

3 Case 3: The Xinchangcheng Block 7 Project in Huangpu District

Since 2017, the CPC municipal committee and municipal government have shifted from prioritizing demolition to prioritizing preservation while advancing demolition, transformation, and preservation. This change introduced the directive to "adhere to the simultaneous implementation of 'preservation, transformation, and demolition', deepen organic urban renewal, and further improve the living conditions of citizens".

The Xinchangcheng Block 7 Project (Fig. 4) comprises a vast area of old housing transformation, while also serving as a historical character protection block. Based on a thorough character assessment, the project tailored renewal approaches for historic buildings on the site in the planning stage, choosing to restore historic buildings worth conservation either in place or at alternative locations while preserving the historical layout of lanes and the facades, structural elements, and other visual and spatial characteristics of other historic buildings. (Fig. 5). During the implementation of this project, the management authorities innovated a "red-black map" as a guiding standard for character protection management throughout the entire process, rein-

Fig. 4 Aerial View of the Design Scheme of the Xinchangcheng Block 7 Project

Fig. 5 Retention of valuable components

forcing closed-loop management for character protection across various stages such as planning, demolition, and construction management.

The three cases mentioned above illustrate the evolution of Shanghai's continuous efforts to strengthen the protection of historic buildings and character. In recent years, while implementing the six major urban renewal initiatives, Shanghai has firmly embraced the guiding principle of integrating preservation, transformation, and demolition. The city strives to safeguard its cultural essence and preserve its cultural roots. It is accelerating the advancement of several key projects, aiming to establish a series of sustainable and replicable renewal models.

4 Case 4: Panlong Tiandi Urban Village Transformation Project in Qingpu District

While over 4,000 outstanding historic buildings have been well-protected, the protection of historical character has expanded from the city center to suburban ancient towns.

The Panlong Historical and Cultural Landscape within the project is one of the 44 historical and cultural landscapes in Shanghai (Fig. 6 and Fig. 7). The project is the last among the first batch of urban village transformation projects in Shanghai to receive approval and the first to be completed as a demonstration project. The project introduced Shui On Group as a partner to deeply explore the cultural history of Panlong Town for more than 1,400 years, restore the city scape such as "Ten Views of Panlong", protect and continue the street and alley, historic buildings and historical environment of the ancient town, and reproduce the heritage of the waterside ancient town by combining contemporary elements. The project resettled the indigenous villagers nearby and improved their living conditions, while maintaining their emotional ties with the region so that they can share the transformation results.

Fig. 6 Rendering of the Panlong Tiandi Urban Village Transformation Project

Chapter III Shared Space and Infrastructure Construction

Fig. 7　Real Scene of Panlong Tiandi

5　Case 5: Hongkou District 167 block Ruikangli project

Hongkou District People's Government and Shanghai Land (Group) Co., Ltd. took Ruikangli Heritage Conservation Neighborhoods (Fig. 8) as a pilot project to explore a new urban renewal model and a new mechanism of capital balance, which can improve the quality of the city, continue the historical context, share the transformation costs and realize the coexistence between old and new residents. In August this year, the project completed a round of inquiries with a high proportion of 99.69%.

Fig. 8　Renderings of the street facade of Rekonli

The exploration of Ruikangli marks the development from a simple focus on the protection of historic buildings as "things" to the overall heritage protection of "things and people". To achieve this goal, the project has carried out explorations and breakthroughs in models and mechanisms: First, through the voluntary application of residents, provide multiple resettlement channels such as vacation, nearby rental exchange, leaseback, repurchase and common property rights; Second, maintain the heritage of Shikumen Lilong Residences, continue the urban context, adhere to high-quality construction and improve public facilities; Third, encourage the coexistence between new and old residents in the neighborhood through multiple resettlement methods such as leaseback, repurchase and mixed property rights; Fourth, give full play to the role of financial leverage and shared transformation costs through institutional innovation to effectively reduce costs and achieve long-term basic balance.

6 Case 6: The Neighborhood 160 Old Municipal Government Building protective renovation project in Huangpu District

The Neighborhood 160 Old Municipal Government Building in Huangpu District (Fig. 9 and Fig. 10) is a cultural relic protection unit of Shanghai. Before the renewal, its supporting facilities were outdated, its internal structure was chaotic, and there were problems such as different degrees of construction, which seriously affected the protection of cultural relics and historical characters. In 2019, it took the lead in starting construction as a municipal demonstration project of urban renewal and a pilot project of "the second facade" on the Bund.

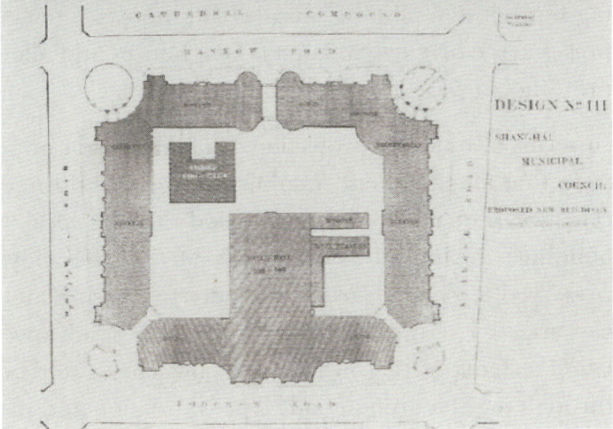

Fig. 9 Old Municipal Government Building before Transformation

Chapter III Shared Space and Infrastructure Construction

Fig. 10 Old Municipal Government Building after Transformation

Originally designed as an enclosed building, the Old Municipal Government Building remained semi-enclosed with gaps when it was completed in 1922. Through this renewal, the gaps are filled against the original design drawings, and the architectural enclosure in the initial design of the century-old building is re-implemented.

7 Case 7: Protective renewal project of Zhang Garden in Jing 'an District

Zhang Garden in Jing'an District (Fig. 11) is located in the West Nanjing Road Historical and Cultural Area. After the 1920s, Zhang Garden has successively built more than 170 Shikumen buildings of 28 types and different styles. It is one of the existing largest, most complete and richest architectural complexes in Shanghai, known as "the first famous garden on the sea". The project was renewed in the way of "requisitioning but not demolishing, and leaving houses after people leave". It tried its best to preserve the original Shikumen lane houses and alleys, which is a new model for the protection of vast stretches of lane houses.

In terms of building protection, Zhang Garden implemented "embroidery needle"-style fine management, established "one building, one policy and one plan" for classified protection, and formulated the first local standard for the care of historic buildings. Technically, since nearly 90% of the above-ground historic buildings are preserved in Zhang Garden, in order to develop and utilize underground space, the east area of Zhang Garden adopted the most advanced "walking" architectural translation technology (Fig. 12) in China, which realized both protection and development through the "Huarong Road" type translation and movement.

Fig. 11　Interior of Zhang Garden after Transformation

Fig. 12　"Walking" Translation Technique

8　Case 8: The Shangsheng·Xinsuo Renewal Project in Changning District

The Shangsheng·Xinsuo Project in Changning District is a representative of the expansion of conservation and renewal types from vast stretches of residential lane houses to industrial parks and commercial offices. After a century of historical evo-

Chapter III　Shared Space and Infrastructure Construction

lution, there are protected buildings such as Sunke Villa (Fig. 13), Colombia Country Club, Navy Club and affiliated swimming pools (Fig. 14), as well as 11 industrial building remains and 4 contemporary buildings in the park. In the process of renewal, a tailored transformation plan was made for each building. Representative build-

Fig. 13 Former Residence of Sun Ke

Fig. 14 Navy Club and affiliated swimming pools

ings in various periods are respected to protect the hard-won architectural diversity to the greatest extent. The concept of "promoting protection with utilization" is fully embodied in the project. The implementer carries out renewal and operation by long-term leasing from property owners, organically combining commercial real estate operation management with historic building protection.

9 Case 9: Zhangjiang Cement Factory Industrial Heritage Renewal Project in Pudong New Area

Zhangjiang Cement Plant in Pudong New Area (Fig. 15) is located within the "Golden Middle Ring Development Belt" of Pudong New Area, formerly known as Chuansha Smelter founded in 1971, with unique industrial remains. On the basis of preserving historic buildings such as "10,000-meter warehouse", "silo" and "kiln tail", it has been transformed and developed into a compound industrial park with industrial coexistence, diversified architecture and cultural sharing (Fig. 16). The project invited 12

Fig. 15 Aerial View of Zhangjiang Cement Plant Project Scheme in Pudong New Area

Fig. 16 The architectural renovation plans of renowned masters at home and abroad

Chapter III Shared Space and Infrastructure Construction

well-known masters at home and abroad to jointly design, fully demonstrating the co-existence of architectural art. The concept of "promoting protection with utilization" has been widely recognized by society and extended to the preservation of special forms of industrial heritage.

10 Case 10: The Riverside Landscape Improvement Project of Huazheng Section of Suzhou Creek in Changning District

In 2021, on the basis of connecting the public space of Suzhou Creek, Changning District eliminated the physical separation between the footpath along the creek and the Campus of East China University of Political Science and Law and created 10 landscapes in the public space to take the overall character of the Campus of East China University of Political Science and Law as part of the landscape along the Suzhou Creek. In 2022, the integration and opening-up of the Campus of East China University of Political Science and Law and Zhongshan Park were further promoted to create an unseparated slow traffic space network. The concept of historical and cultural protection and preservation was further expanded to the "one river, one creek" area (Fig. 17).

Fig. 17 Waterfront Open Space of Suzhou Creek after Transformation

2023 is the initial year for Shanghai to comprehensively promote the implementation of urban renewal actions. Shanghai will practice the concept of the people-centered city. In implementing urban renewal, it will strive to protect and inherit its historical context, retain urban memory, provide emotional sustenance for the people, and draw a vivid picture of high-quality development, high-quality life and efficient governance.

Chapter IV

Human-oriented Urban Development and Soft Power Enhancement

Structural Mismatch and Governance in the Housing Rental Market in China's Large Cities[1]

Yu Xiaofen
President of the China Academy of Housing & Real Estate at the Zhejiang University of Technology

This is an excerpt from the author's speech at the Housing Rental Symposium.

The rapid pace and sheer scale of urbanization in China have created a wonder in human history. By 2023, the total urban population nationwide had reached 933 million, with a net increase of 263 million since 2010 and 742 million since 1980. Amidst this demographic shift, a substantial demand for rental housing has emerged, with over 200 million individuals currently relying on rental accommodations, constituting the world's largest housing rental market. China's housing rental market has transitioned from purely market-driven behavior to substantial government policy support, moving from disorder to order. This transformation has effectively addressed the housing difficulties faced by a significant number of new urban residents. However, due to the large scale of new citizens and high housing prices in large cities, the mismatch between supply and demand in the housing rental market remains serious and needs to be improved.

1 Changes in Demographic Structure and Development of the Housing Rental Market

1.1 Four development stages of China's housing rental market
With the increase in population mobility and rental population, China has paid more and more attention to the housing rental market, which can be divided into the following four stages.

(1) Unorganized development stage (before 2011). At that time, there was virtually no organized and planned government support for the rental housing market. Low-rent housing for low-income groups with housing difficulties requires all local departments to raise market-oriented housing resources and monetization.

---

[1] This paper is an intermediate achievement of the National Natural Science Foundation of China (72274176).

(2) Initial organized development stage (2011—2014). In this stage, marked by the release of Guiding Opinions on Accelerating the Development of Public Rental Housing (GBF [2010] No. 4), the government began to take the initiative to increase low-rent public rental housing, aiming to solve the housing difficulties of urban low-income and middle-low income families. On the one hand, local governments were required to invest in construction; on the other hand, various investment entities were encouraged and guided to build houses for employees or workers in industrial parks. During this period, there was a boom in the construction of public rental housing. In particular, some large enterprises raised funds to build dormitories for employees, solving the housing difficulties of some middle-low income families and new citizens. Unfortunately, due to the lack of relevant support policies, enterprises gradually withdrew from the construction of public rental housing.

(3) Cultivation and development stage (2015-2019). In 2015, China made it clear that a housing system of "promoting renting and purchasing simultaneously" should be established. In 2016, the General Office of the State Council issued Several Opinions on Accelerating the Cultivation and Development of Housing Rental Market (GBF [2016] No. 39), which put forward implementation opinions from such aspects as cultivating market suppliers, encouraging housing rental consumption, supporting the construction of rental housing and increasing policy support. Subsequently, the central government provided special financial support for 24 major cities; financial institutions also increased credit support for housing rental projects; housing provident funds fully supported rental withdrawals; and the government introduced tax support policies to support the development of specialized rental enterprises. A number of specialized rental enterprises emerged in large cities. They actively innovated project-raising methods, products and services to promote the development of local housing rental markets.

(4) Accelerated development stage (2020-now). Although all regions have begun to attach importance to the development of the rental market, there are still a large number of new citizens and young people in large cities in China who cannot afford or rent houses. Many people live in urban villages in the downtown areas, old communities, and shantytowns. If there is a large number of public rental housing construction, the government finances are difficult to bear; additionally, the low-rent and small rental housing supply in the market is seriously insufficient. Therefore, in 2021, the country further issued the Opinions on Accelerating the Development of Indemnificatory Rental Housing (GBF [2021] No. 22), which clarifies that the government will further increase support for land use, taxation, finance, and civilian water and electricity prices, encourage market-oriented institutions to increase the supply of rental housing with the prices slightly below the market rental price, and alleviate the structural problems of the housing rental market. By September 2023, a total of 5.08 million indemnificatory rental housing units had been raised nationwide.

1.2 The population continues to gather in large cities, and there is a great demand for rental housing in large cities

The trend of population concentration in large cities is obvious, and the housing rental market has formed a huge scale. According to the data of the Seventh National Population Census (hereinafter referred to as the "Seventh Census"), from 2011 to 2020, Shenzhen, Chengdu, Guangzhou, Zhengzhou, Xi'an, Hangzhou, Chongqing, and Changsha have an average annual increase in permanent population of more than 300,000. Rental households account for more than 30% of the permanent residents in Beijing, Shanghai, Hangzhou, Ningbo, and Suzhou. See Tab. 1. In 2022, the number of people renting houses in Beijing was about 7.3 million, more than one-third of the city's population. However, there are only 2 million housing units for rent in the city, and 150,000 college graduates enter the rental market every year. Shanghai has a permanent resident population of 24.871 million and about 9.95 million renters, but there are only about 157,000 centralized long-term rental apartments under institutionalized operation in stock. The total amount of rental housing suitable for new citizens and young people in large cities is still insufficient. We should fully realize the importance of developing rental market and solve housing problems in large cities by actively developing rental market.

Tab. 1 Household size and rent proportion in some large cities during the Seventh National Population Census

No.	City	Number of Permanent Households in 2020	Proportion of Rental Households in the Permanent Households in 2020 /%
1	Shanghai	9 095 041	38.74
2	Beijing	7 770 769	35.44
3	Chengdu	7 076 572	22.40
4	Hangzhou	4 113 283	40.42
5	Xi'an	4 050 039	23.13
6	Suzhou	3 918 580	30.12
7	Ningbo	3 618 432	40.68
8	Zhengzhou	3 481 832	20.00

Source: The Sixth and Seventh National Population Census.

1.3 Development achievements of rental housing market in large cities

With the strong support of national policies, China's housing rental market has developed rapidly, which is mainly reflected in four aspects: First, the scale of the rental housing market is expanding and the level of housing rent is generally stable. Second, the institutionalized rental entities continue to grow. A number of institutionalized rental entities have emerged, which play an important role in the healthy development of the rental market. In 2022, a total of 627,700 rooms were opened by the top 10 enterprises, marking a 2.63% year-on-year increase. A total of 4 Real Estate Investment Trusts (REITs) were issued and listed in 2022, with a cumulative scale of RMB 5.005 billion, achieving a breakthrough from 0 to 1 in the REIT sector. Third, the development of indemnificatory rental housing has achieved phased results, and more than 10 million new citizens and young people have been provided with comfortable housing. Fourth, the living quality of rental housing has been greatly improved. After the renovation of shantytowns and urban villages, a significant number of high-quality rental housing has taken their place. Notably, institutionalized long-term rental apartments (both centralized and decentralized) now offer standardized, diverse, and high-quality housing that meets the needs of new urban residents and young people seeking to live well. Consequently, the overall living standards in urban housing have seen substantial improvements. For example, in the ten urban districts of Hangzhou, the per capita housing area for non-Hangzhou household renters has reached $25m^2$.

2 Mismatch in the Housing Rental Market in Large Cities

While we fully acknowledge the accomplishments made, it is essential to recognize that the housing rental market in large cities still faces significant mismatches. There remains a considerable journey ahead to effectively develop this market.

2.1 Regional mismatch

It is primarily evident in the significant structural issues of "oversupply" or "undersupply" of rental housing within cities. Taking Hangzhou as an example, if every individual renting a house in the administrative region has a living space of 25 m^2 and 40% of the employed population in the region can reside locally, big data calculations reveal a significant supply gap in Gongshu District, Xihu District, Binjiang District, and the old Shangcheng District. In contrast, Lin'an District, Linping District, and Fuyang District have ample housing supply.

2.2 Work-home mismatch

The separation of work and home locations increases urban operating costs and affects people's overall satisfaction. Taking Hangzhou as an example, there is a work-home imbalance among renters in many districts. For instance, less than 30% of the employees in Gongshu, Xihu, Binjiang, and Shangcheng Districts reside locally.

2.3 Quality mismatch

The traditional housing rental market often faces mismatches in both housing quality and service quality. The expectations of new urban residents and young people regarding living conditions have shifted from simply having a place to live to demanding a certain level of quality. Based on Ziroom's research, over 25% of tenants independently purchase cleaning services and more than 50% buy maintenance services on their own. Due to Ziroom's provision of professional services in Hangzhou, the average transaction cycle for its rental housing is 32 days, which is 11 days shorter than the cycle for ordinary rental housing.

2.4 Price mismatch

In Hangzhou, rental affordability is approximately RMB 1,000 per room per month for new migrant workers, and around RMB 2,000 per room per month for college students. However, there is a shortage of suitable low- and medium-priced housing options that offer independent living spaces.

2.5 Housing type mismatch

Using Hangzhou as an example, the demand for one-bedroom rental housing exceeds 60%, yet the market supply for such housing is less than 20%. Conversely, the supply of two-bedroom and larger rental housing surpasses the current demand. According to Ziroom's data, Beijing has approximately 710,000 houses with three or more bedrooms, comprising 30% of the total housing. While the overall supply is substantial, renting out entire houses remains challenging. The occupancy rate for entire three-bedroom or larger housing in Beijing, Shanghai, Guangzhou, and Shenzhen has consistently been lower compared to shared rentals and one- or two-bedroom housing. This illustrates the supply-demand mismatch in housing types.

3 Governance of Housing Rental Market Mismatch in Large Cities

3.1 Optimize land use planning and coordinate the relationship between life and production

The ratio of industrial land to residential land should be optimized to maintain a balance between work and home, actively fostering the development of industrial communities. Taking the mixed community in Ningbo Hangzhou Bay New Zone as an example, during the land use planning stage, the mixed community was designed based on the number and composition of the employed population. It integrates centralized rental housing, marketable housing, living facilities, entertainment and leisure options, and business meeting spaces, ensuring it meets the diverse resident needs for living, working, and business activities. The layout should be as compact as possible while meeting evacuation requirements and prioritizing convenience.

3.2 Adhere to public transport-oriented development

Inspiration can be drawn from Japan's experience. Centralized rental housing in the country is typically located near subway stations, Shinkansen lines, and bus stops, offering convenient travel options. Statistics indicate that 64.14% of public tenants in Japan have a daily commute of 30 minutes or less, significantly higher than the 49.10% of homeowners with similar commute times.

3.3 Accelerate the development of rental housing

With an unwavering commitment to safety, housing renovations proceed based on willingness and feasibility. Various channels should be actively explored to diversify project types. These include supporting land for industrial parks, collective operational construction land, village-level retained land, centralized collection, storage, and transformation of rural resettlement housing, and reconstruction of non-residential stock housing. The government, enterprises, village communities, villagers, and banks should be fully mobilized to establish a comprehensive five-party governance system involving all these stakeholders. This collaboration aims to achieve multi-body supply and encourages employers to share the responsibility of addressing their employees' housing needs.

3.4 Improve the supply system

Republic of Korea's experience provides a valuable reference to support multi-level supply in rental housing market. In Republic of Korea, rental housing makes up over 40% of the total housing stock, offering a variety of levels and types. This includes options tailored for lowest-income and low-income groups, as well as targeted rentals for young people, newlyweds, and the elderly. Both long-term rentals and "rent-to-own" options are available, supported by diverse supply policies that cater to different needs. China could benefit from adopting this multifaceted approach.

3.5 Increase financial support

The housing market in large cities has entered the era of inventory management. In the next phase, it is essential to secure more stable incomes through effective asset management. It is crucial to actively support REITs for housing rental projects and provide developers with new financing channels. Additionally, increasing rental income through proactive asset management will enhance the overall quality of the rental market

3.6 Accelerate the development of legislation and management systems for the rental market

Legislation should establish a policy framework promoting the healthy and stable development of rental housing. This framework aims to standardize practices among rental professionals and institutions while enhancing tenant rights and interests protection.

3.7 Strengthen intelligent, precise, and efficient rental management

Hangzhou has initiated a multi-departmental Big data project to develop an intelligent housing rental platform. This platform considers various factors such as rental, population, land, housing, and guarantee to achieve integrated intelligent management and precise decision-making concerning "people, housing, and land". This approach serves as a valuable model for reference and promotion throughout China.

Promoting the Integration of Treatment, Prevention, Health Management and Care for the Aged to Comprehensively Improve Healthcare Capability

Li Hui[*] Xu Jiayu[**] Yan Hua[***]

[*] Chief Physician, Deputy Director of Xietu Community Healthcare Center, Xuhui, Shanghai, China
[**] Associate Chief Physician, Office Director of Xietu Community Healthcare Center, Xuhui, Shanghai, China
[***] Associate Chief Physician, Director of Xuhui Senior Nursing Hospital, Shanghai, China

This is an excerpt from the author's speech at the Integration of Treatment, Prevention, Health Management and Care for the Aged - 'World Cities Day' Geriatric Rehabilitation Collaborative Exchange Meeting in Shanghai, China in 2023.

With the acceleration of urbanization, the aging problem in cities is becoming increasingly severe. The quality of life and healthcare demand of the elderly have become the focus of social attention. As the cornerstone of urban healthcare services, the Community Healthcare Center (Hereinafter referred to as the Center) plays an important role in disease prevention, medical treatment, health management, and elderly care.

1 Profile of the Center

1.1 Historical Connotations and Modern Transformation

Established in 1937, the Center was formerly known as Bethel Maternity Hospital and renamed as Rihui Hospital (Grade B Secondary Hospital) in December 1960. In May 2004, in response to the community health reform, it was transformed into Xietu Subdistrict Community Healthcare Center (Fig. 1). In recent years, the Center has been committed to improving the quality of medical services and the medical experience for patients. In March 2021, the layout and the processes were improved for the Center to realize zoning management and parallel services for community medical care and health management, providing patients with a more convenient and comfortable environment for medical treatment.

1.2 Service Scope and Population Coverage

The Center is located in the northeast area of Xuhui District, with a service area of 3.18 km^2 and 19 Residents Committees. It serves a permanent resident population of over 71,000, with a significant proportion of elderly residents. The Center spans

Fig. 1　Xietu Community Healthcare Center

14,660.38 m^2 and accommodates 193 approved beds (including elderly care beds, rehabilitation beds, and palliative care beds), so as to meet the diversified health needs of the elderly population. In addition, to ensure comprehensive coverage and convenience of medical services, the Center has set up 5 standardized Community Healthcare Clinics.

1.3 Service Optimization and Development Prospects

Leveraging the high-quality medical resources of Zhongshan Hospital and Xuhui District Central Hospital within the Integrated Medical System, the Center has achieved significant progress in discipline development, research and teaching. At present, the Center's diagnosis and treatment services encompass internal medicine, surgery, gynecology, and pediatrics. Additionally, the Center provides specialized services in ophthalmology and otolaryngology, stomatology, and dermatology departments, has a team of skilled practitioners in auxiliary test departments (such as ultrasonography, radiology, and ECG), and offers featured clinics for hypertension, diabetes, atrial fibrillation, geriatric pulmonary, mental health, and more. The Center provides the community residents with more convenient and accurate medical services.

Over the years, the Center has won many national and municipal honors for its high-quality medical service capacity and quality, such as National Model Community Healthcare Center, National Quality Service Demonstration Community Healthcare Center, Community Health Service Organization Satisfied by the National Public, The First Batch of Excellent Community Healthcare Centers in Shanghai, and Shanghai Civilized Institution. In 2018, it ranked third in the national list of community medical service institutions. In 2022, the Center was rated as an Excellent Service Brand Institution of Shanghai Age-friendly Medical Institutions and selected as a Pilot Institution for High-quality Development of Public Hospitals in Shanghai. Seizing this opportunity, the Center further refined its functional orientation, enhanced its service quality, and elevated its development standards.

2 Community Rehabilitation Services

The Center is committed to building a comprehensive and efficient rehabilitation service system to meet the growing rehabilitation needs of community residents through continuous innovative practice, rehabilitation concept updates, service system improvement, and rehabilitation brand creation.

2.1 Exploring a Diversified Community Rehabilitation Service System

(1) Improve the Service System and Build a Full-chain Rehabilitation Network. Based on both outpatient and inpatient rehabilitation services, the Center has gradually extended rehabilitation services to community healthcare clinics, homes and elderly care institutions by combining Traditional Chinese Medicine (TCM) with Western Medicine. The Center has set up a coherent full-chain rehabilitation network that spans "ward-outpatient-station-home", which significantly enhances the continuity and effectiveness of services and ensures that patients can receive timely and professional support at different stages of rehabilitation.

(2) Building a Comprehensive Service Team and Optimizing the Intelligent Rehabilitation Equipment. By optimizing the team structure, the Center has established a professional rehabilitation service team composed of rehabilitation physicians, rehabilitation therapists, rehabilitation nurses, and TCM physicians. Additionally, it has guided general practitioners and TCM physicians to participate in municipal rehabilitation training, thereby continuously staffing the community-based rehabilitation team. The Center has introduced modern and intelligent equipment for rehabilitation (such as intelligent robots, ceiling hoist mobile systems, and rehabilitation evaluation and training systems) to meet the actual rehabilitation needs of elderly patients and further improve service accuracy and treatment efficiency. At present, the Center averagely serves 180 residents per day and provides 42 rehabilitation services including various evaluations.

2.2 Building a Featured Brand of Community-based Rehabilitation Services

The Center actively promotes the development of a featured brand for the rehabilitation of chronic diseases in the elderly. Addressing the needs of residents, it emphasizes the development of featured disciplines (such as cardiac rehabilitation and respiratory rehabilitation), along with various sub-disciplines (such as cerebrovascular diseases, acute and chronic pain, peripheral nerve diseases, and senile degenerative diseases). Leveraging the platform of the Integrated Medical System, the Center has enhanced interdisciplinary collaboration, streamlined two-way referrals, and invited experts from higher-level medical institutions to engage with local communities. This initiative has promoted the optimal allocation and sharing of rehabilitation medical resources in the region, facilitated the homogenization of rehabilitation services, and provided a robust foundation for residents' health.

3 Medical and Preventive Integration

3.1 Building a Comprehensive Health Management System with Family Doctors as the Core

The family doctor contracting system was first implemented in Shanghai as a key strategy to improve community health and residents' well-being. Since 2011, the Center has vigorously promoted family doctor services. Leveraging the family doctor team as a bridge, it has extended health services to every family by deepening medical and prevention integration, strengthening the development of family doctor teams, innovating service models, and emphasizing the core concept of Treatment Based on Prioritized Prevention. This approach has facilitated a significant transition from simple Disease Treatment to comprehensive Health Management.

Facing the challenges of population aging and changes in the structure and function of community families, the Center leverages the model worker studio of Zhu Lan, a representative family doctor, to focus on community families. This initiative aims to enhance the services provided by family doctor contracts, continuously improve the elderly care capabilities of family members, and explore a new smart elderly mode for the combination of health and care that integrates medical treatment, elderly care, nursing, rehabilitation, and life care at home. At the same time, various service modes of the Center and elderly care institutions will be explored to ensure that all elderly care institutions, day-care centers, and nursing stations in the community are included in the contracting service network and the effective supply of health services.

3.2 Developing a New Model of One-stop Health Services that Integrates Medical Care and Disease Prevention

Considering chronic disease management's long-term and complex nature, the Center leverages information technology and is bolstered by professional voluntary services to enhance service capabilities. By comprehensively integrating various health service resources (such as medical treatment, nursing, public health, rehabilitation services, and health education), the Center aims to establish a comprehensive and multi-level health management service system, so as to offer one-stop health management services from prevention, screening, diagnosis, and treatment to rehabilitation for patients with chronic diseases.

3.2.1 Expand service functions and focus on promoting the development of Three Centers

(1) Health Management Center. It provides many intelligent technologies (such as accurate blood pressure measurement monitoring, intelligent blood glucose, BMI rapid measurement, standardized lung function examination, self-help screening of fecal occult blood for colorectal cancer, and AI voice follow-up), which can realize the accurate collection and monitoring of comprehensive risk factors of chronic diseases and provide comprehensive and efficient health management services for patients with chronic diseases. The Health Management Center strictly implements the Responsibility System with Simplified Procedure and realizes efficient integration of resources

through assigned personnel to significantly improve the efficiency of full-cycle management of chronic diseases. The team focuses on providing high-quality diagnosis and treatment services, serving more than 13,000 residents in total. In addition, the Center conducts health assessments and targeted health intervention for contracted residents, based on family doctor contracting services. In terms of intelligent management, the Health Management Center has actively used information technology to develop and implement various targeted prevention and control strategies for chronic diseases, with excellent performance. In 2022, the Center passed the acceptance by Shanghai Chronic Disease Management Center and was awarded Excellent Construction Institution (Fig. 2).

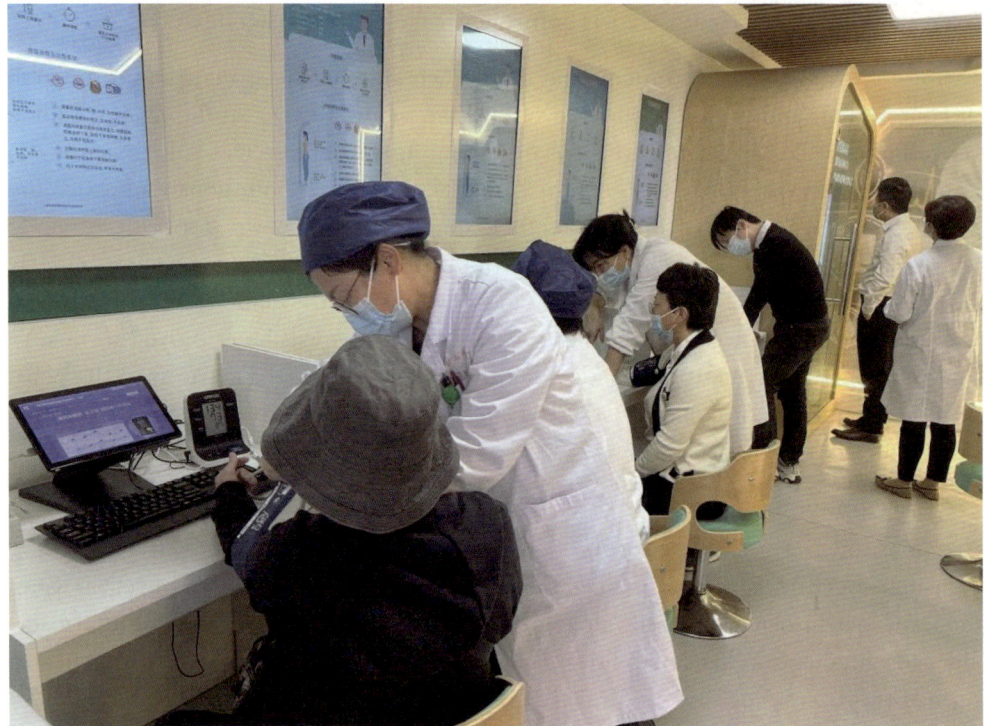

Fig. 2 Health Management Center

(2) Rehabilitation Center. The Rehabilitation Center covers over 1,300 m² and includes 2 areas: the exercise treatment area and the physical factor treatment area, catering to meet the rehabilitation needs of different patients. The Rehabilitation Center adopts a team-based approach and integrates both TCM and Western Medicine treatment methods, actively cultivates featured rehabilitations (such as respiratory rehabilitation and cardiac rehabilitation), and develops an innovative rehabilitation model known as Integration of Rehabilitation and Sports. Leveraging the Featured Demonstration Service Clinic of Traditional Chinese Medicine of Shanghai, the Rehabilitation Center aims to further develop TCM-specific rehabilitation services. By enhancing the "five-in-one" service model, the Center extends its rehabilitation services from outpatient and ward to community stations and homes. This approach ensures broad coverage and deep integration of rehabilitation services, offering patients a

comprehensive and continuous rehabilitation service experience. In October 2022, the Rehabilitation Center was successfully rated as the Shanghai Demonstration Community Rehabilitation Center (Fig. 3).

(3) Nursing Center. The Nursing Center is located on the south side of the fourth floor of the outpatient department, with an area of 126 m². It has independent functional areas (such as rooms for wound care, diabetes care, PICC /PORT catheter maintenance, palliative care, and nursing consultation) to meet the diversified nursing needs of patients. Leveraging the establishment of one of Shanghai Women's Innovation Studios and based on family doctor contracting services, a 15-minute nursing circle has been created to provide extended and home care for discharged patients, chronic disease patients, and elderly patients. The "Circle for Education and Awareness and Circle for Quality Control" nursing project has been approved for the Circle for Quality Control by the Shanghai Hospital Association in 2024 (Fig. 4).

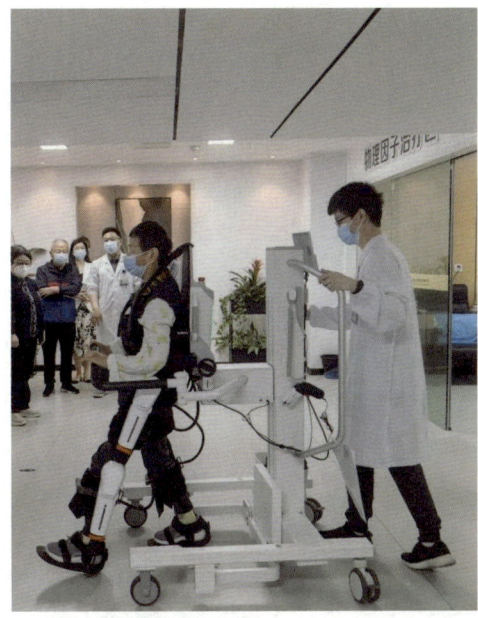

Fig.3　Rehabilitation Center

Fig. 4　Nursing Center and Nursing Team

Chapter IV Human-oriented Urban Development and Soft Power Enhancement

3.2.2 Improve the Mechanism of Medical Social Workers and Volunteer Services

Fig. 5 Volunteer Service

The Center is committed to deepening the combination of medical social work and primary healthcare services, and has established a volunteer team led by experienced and full-time clinical medical social workers. The Center actively explores the multi-professional team (MPT) cooperation model by integrating resources from various disciplines (such as medical treatment, nursing, and social work) and comprehensively using the professional knowledge and methods of medical social work, so as to help patients and their families in need alleviate, solve, and prevent medical social problems (Fig. 5).

The Center values volunteer service and the training and education of social work talents. It has established close cooperative relations with well-known universities worldwide, establishing itself as a volunteer base for Tulane University and other universities. This partnership injects fresh enthusiasm into volunteer services and offers invaluable practical platforms for students. As a social work teaching practice base, the Center also undertakes the important task of providing practical opportunities and professional guidance for students majoring in social work. By participating in the daily services and professional projects of the Center, students can learn and master the professional skills and methods of social work in practice, thus laying a solid foundation for their future careers.

3.2.3 Use Smart Diagnosis and Treatment to Facilitate Elderly-friendly Medical Services

(1) Telehealth and Multidisciplinary Consultation Improve the Convenience of Medical Treatment. The Center has continuously strengthened the information construction of remote diagnosis and treatment to provide diversified and convenient medical services for the elderly. Through the improvement of relevant systems, a set of information management system and service model in line with the features of geriatrics have been established to ensure the professionalism and efficiency of services. By making use of the compact and project-based Integrated Medical System in the community, the efficient operation of Xuhui Cloud Hospital (a comprehensive and specialized cloud platform), and normalized telehealth and multidisciplinary consultations, the Center greatly improves the convenience of community contracted elderly people to see a doctor and provides them with comprehensive and reliable health management services (Fig. 6).

(2) Services of the Combination of Health and Care and Remote Collaboration Make

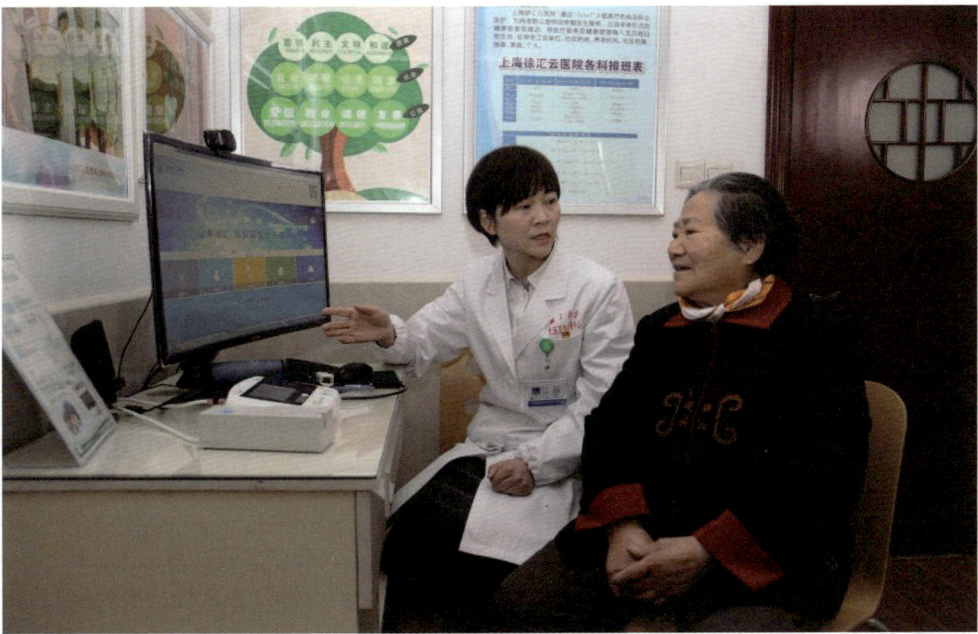

Fig. 6　Remote Diagnosis and Treatment

Healthcare Accessible. As the "National Pilot Institution for Services of the Combination of Health and Care and Remote Collaboration for Elderly Health", Rihui Nursing Home in the Center covers expert services of 7 departments (such as respiratory, neurology, and urology) through remote collaboration. It provides all-round telehealth support for hospitalized elderly with mobility difficulties, so that they can conveniently obtain professional medical advice and health guidance.

3.2.4 Teaching and Learning Interact Positively and Make the Concept of Serving the Elderly Rooted

As a teaching base for many higher medical education institutions, the Center undertakes the noble mission of cultivating future medical talents. The Center is a general medicine community teaching base for standardized training of resident physicians in Shanghai, a community practice base for standardized cultivation of TCM general practitioners in Shanghai, a preventive medicine community internship base at the School of Public Health of Fudan University, and a community teaching base at the Shanghai Sixth People's Hospital Affiliated to Shanghai Jiao Tong University for standardized training of resident physicians in Shanghai. With Serving the Elderly as its core teaching concept, the Center closely integrates geriatrics with community services. Through diversified teaching methods (such as clinical internships, case studies, and community research), students can deeply understand the medical needs of elderly patients in practice. This approach can foster their humanistic care spirit, and ensure that the concept of Serving the Elderly is both deeply understood and applied in practice.

Optimizing Property Governance Structure to Create High-quality Century-long Housing

Cheng Peng
Professor, Doctoral Supervisor, and Head of the Department of Property Management of the School of Economics & Management, Beijing Forestry University, Member of the Professional Committee on Community Construction of the Ministry of Housing and Urban-Rural Development

This is an excerpt from the author's speech at the China Urban High-quality Development Forum.

Facing the current predicaments in the property management industry, it would be overly simplistic to attribute the issues solely to inadequate service quality or insufficient property management by property companies. Instead, the entire property governance system is at fault, and the solutions to these problems extend beyond the responsibilities and capabilities of the property management industry. Therefore, what we need is to optimize the existing property management structure.

Property management, as the name suggests, focuses on managing properties as objects and content of services. In contemporary terms, the management of all buildings includes both human and physical aspects. The term "physical management" refers to the preservation, improvement, utilization, and disposal of buildings, sites, and related facilities, primarily limited to common areas of buildings, excluding exclusive areas. Compared to traditional property management, modern property management has significantly expanded beyond the mere maintenance, upkeep, and management of buildings in terms of scope and depth. Yet, this evolution does not diminish the core value and importance of property facilities management services.

The essence of property management lies in the comprehensive maintenance and effective management of buildings. Understanding the essential attributes of property management is the logical starting point for property management reform. In property management, the management of "physical objects" encompasses regular maintenance and repairs, the operation and management of facilities and equipment, as well as ensuring safety and maintaining environmental cleanliness. Through scientific management methods and professional service teams, property management guarantees the long-term sustainable operation of buildings and the continuous appreciation of asset value. All business development and commercial expansion within the property management industry revolve around or are linked to property facilities. Without the solid support of property facilities management as a fundamental service, any innovation in property management services would struggle to achieve true success. Property facilities management is not only the foundation for the stable development of the property management industry but also the essential positioning of the professional value of property management.

Property management essentially refers to the public services within a residential community and possesses a dual nature of both private and public products, with the core business of property management exhibiting externalities. While serving as a bridge between owners and property service companies and playing a crucial role in maintaining the quality and value of buildings, property management still faces many challenges in practice. Especially in the context of rapid industrial development and the trend toward delicacy management in urban renewal and transformation, the self-regulating function of the market does not always operate effectively, and social regulatory forces have not been fully in place. On one hand, owners often exhibit low satisfaction with property services, while property management companies face issues such as owner distrust, inconsistent service standards, and varying management capabilities. On the other hand, the property service market frequently experiences low entry barriers, inadequate market access and regulation, information asymmetry, and a lack of effective incentive and constraint mechanisms. Moreover, the relationship between owners and property service companies is not a one-to-one association but rather a one-to-many connection, where the limited bidirectional constraints between owners and property service companies result in incomplete property service contracts.

Due to the uneven and unstable development of social and market forces, their dysfunction, absence of roles, or imbalanced relationships with other governance entities in governance can lead to the failure of residential community governance. To alleviate this conflict, on one hand, it is necessary to improve property service contracts so that they can adapt to various stages of the residential community life cycle. This includes enhancing the division of responsibilities and standard regulations for the maintenance and upkeep of the properties themselves, clearly defining the service scope of the property company and the responsibilities of the owners, and fairly allocating the rights and obligations of both parties. On the other hand, as the upholder of order, the government must take measures to maintain the normal order of residential communities. It is also necessary to establish effective communication and coordination mechanisms to promptly address and resolve the owners' property service issues arising from the aging of residential communities, as well as establish a long-term mechanism for maintaining aging properties. Furthermore, laws must enforce standardized and transparent property services and must constrain owner behavior.

Previously, the Ministry of Housing and Urban-Rural Development and other departments jointly issued the *Notice on Strengthening and Improving the Management of Residential Property*, which outlined the establishment of a system of information disclosure and public notification. It specified that property management companies should, under the guidance and supervision of sub-districts, set up prominently located property service information supervision bulletin boards in the property service area. These bulletin boards should truthfully disclose and regularly update the basic information and contact details of the property project leader, property service complaint hotline, property service content and standards, fee items and standards, elevator and fire facilities maintenance units and contact information, parking garage usage, allocation of public utility costs, property fees, income and expenditure related to common areas of owners, elevator maintenance expenses, and other relevant information. The information can also be communicated to owners through various means like online platforms.

The question that needs to be considered is: what exactly does the system of information disclosure and public notification include? As part of this industry, the system of information disclosure and public notification encompasses financial transparency, maintenance records of housing facilities, safety inspection reports, and feedback on property service quality. The financial transparency expected by owners also raises a new issue: how to ensure that money is spent where it should be spent?

The professional value of property management primarily manifests in the following aspects: property facilities management, property asset management, customer relationship management, and customer behavior management. Among these, property facilities management forms the cornerstone of the property management industry, representing the essential positioning of the professional value of property management. It is worth noting that property management services have expanded from merely managing common areas to the management of private properties. Owners not only entrust the management of public spaces to property companies but also delegate related matters within private spaces to professional property management teams. Based on commercial trust and convenience, property companies have a more pronounced professional advantage in conducting property asset management.

In other words, the professional value of property management lies in the subtle and pervasive influence on individuals exerted by property management professionals who systematically maintain and preserve properties within various residential communities in cities, as well as implement standardized management of the behavioral habits of community residents.

Based on the professional value of property management, it is clear that the sustainable development of the property management industry must be built upon the sustainable development of residences. As the real estate market enters a new development cycle, urban renewal and transformation are gradually shifting toward delicacy management. Simultaneously, the increasing number of existing residential communities highlights the growing attention toward housing quality issues. According to statistics, around 80% of existing urban housing in China will be over 30 years old by around 2040. For residential communities with such long housing ages, conducting thorough periodic inspections and assessments is crucial to ensure the structural safety of buildings and the long-term stability of pipeline systems. Therefore, to enhance and prolong the lifespan of building structures, a comprehensive strategy must be adopted to develop multi-level maintenance measures. This requires us to delve into exploring and establishing a system for building maintenance and spatial adaptability that is geared toward future needs, forming a comprehensive and long-term mechanism for housing safety. This system would provide a basis and assurance for the full lifecycle safety management of buildings, effectively "treating" old houses and ensuring their safety.

In the contemporary field of property management services, it is imperative to undergo a fundamental paradigm shift, transitioning from the traditional management model centered around real estate enterprises to a property management and service model with building safety as the core concern. This shift implies that property project management should not be limited solely to the stages of real estate development and transfer but should instead expand to encompass safety maintenance strategies throughout the entire lifecycle of buildings. An ideal property management framework should be based on a thorough consideration of the entire lifecycle of buildings, establishing comprehensive health and safety maintenance plans. In this model, property management services will no longer solely focus on day-to-day maintenance but will also include regular health diagnostics and safety assessment reports at key time nodes throughout the entire lifecycle of the building, starting from its construction to its decommissioning. Throughout this process, periodic health and safety assessments will provide a scientific basis for the continued use of buildings, offering timely guidance and support for various preventive maintenance, emergency maintenance, and structural reinforcement as necessary. Mandatory maintenance plans will not be affected by the change of property management units; their implementation and continuation should be supervised and ensured by the state through the establishment of mandatory standards and regulations.

In the matter of housing repairs and renovations, it is essential to recognize that this involves not only technical expertise but also the well-being and safety of the entire community. The decision-making process for housing repairs cannot solely rely on the personal preferences or wishes of owners because the quality of housing maintenance directly impacts the safety of community residents and their property. The stability of housing structures and the reliability of their functions are the primary tasks in maintaining community safety. Owners' freedom of choice in housing repairs must be reasonably constrained to ensure that maintenance activities do not jeopardize the broader community interests. Therefore, owners need to adhere to a set of mandatory housing repair standards and regulations during housing repairs. The establishment of these standards must be based on in-depth engineering research and risk assessments to ensure the scientific and practical nature of repair work and mitigate any safety risks resulting from improper repairs by employing best practices. The safety of the building itself is a crucial component of community safety and cannot be solely guided by owners' preferences. Compliance with mandatory housing repair standards by owners is a crucial safeguard and tool for building "good houses" and "good communities".

Finally, to ensure the durability of houses and the comprehensive safety of communities, there is an urgent need to establish a sound industry regulatory framework. Within this framework, the formation of social consensus is crucial: firstly, the efficient management of property facilities is the cornerstone of ensuring the stability and rectification of the property industry; secondly, in the responsibility chain of housing repairs, property owners bear the primary and non-delegable responsibility; and lastly, in the various decision-making matters concerning property management, decisions should not solely rely on the personal will of owners but must also consider the interests and safety of the entire community. Efforts should be made to establish a property information disclosure system and housing inspection records for large-scale communities, meticulously documenting the examination history, maintenance records, and condition assessments of each property. This will create a complete residential health record database, enhancing the transparency of property management, making housing sustainability measurable and manageable, and fostering the development of high-quality century-long housing. Furthermore, a decentralized property service regulatory system should be explored and established by leveraging modern technologies such as smart contracts and blockchain, thereby realizing evidence, auditing, and traceability of distributed reliable property service regulation and building a reliable property service regulatory and governance system.

Property management is not just about immediate needs; it involves a comprehensive perspective that has lasting impacts on communities and living environments. We should realize that the improvement of property service quality is not solely the responsibility of property management companies but rather a collective achievement of societal governance as a whole. By improving laws and regulations, strengthening the system of information disclosure and public notification, establishing sound property maintenance mechanisms, and utilizing modern information technology to enhance the transparency and efficiency of property services, we can adapt to evolving market demands, meet the expectations of owners and communities, and ultimately create century-long housing that is not only safe and reliable but also comfortable and livable.

Enhancing Cultural Values of Internet-famous Site Check-in

Xiao Qianhui
President of China Smart Tourism Association

This is an excerpt from the author's speech at the Theme Forum on Protection and Inheritance of Urban History and Culture.

Internet-famous site check-in is a phenomenal trend in today's internet culture. Through meditation, I think this viral and trendy phenomenon lacks some cultural values. Internet-famous site check-in has a distinctive appeal among young people.

1 Whoever Wins the New Generation Will Dominate the Market

The so-called new generation refers to those born in the 80s, 90s, 00s, and 10s. The following three groups of data deserve our attention. The first is their total population and proportion (Tab. 1); the second is that consumers aged below 35 contribute 65% of the economic growth; the third is that Generation Z makes up only 20% of the population but accounts for 40% of the consumption, with this proportion still growing. The new generation has emerged as the primary driving force and leader of social consumption in China. In addition, the new generation has also played a leading role in cultural consumption. To take command of the present and future, it is necessary to understand, get close to, and uplift the new generation.

Tab. 1 Population and proportion of the people born in the 80s, 90s, 00s, and 10s

Age group	Population /100 million	Proportion /%
Post-80s	2.15	15.23
Post-90s	1.78	12.60
Post-00s	1.55	10.98
Post-10s	1.74	12.32
Total	7.22	51.13

2 Whoever Wins Check-in Influencers Will Dominate the Market

Recently, internet-famous site check-in has gone viral. This trend is evidenced by the emergence of attractions such as Zibo Barbecue and Chongqing Liziba Station's through-building train. These attractions have become crowded with tourists, significantly boosting the city's popularity and reputation. Fengxian is home to many popular attractions such as "Fish of Shanghai" and "Oriens Lumina", drawing large numbers of tourists. I've been pondering a question: The new generation comprises a large group of young people with excellent educational backgrounds. Will they visit internet-famous sites? While teaching at Fudan University, I conducted a specialized classroom survey on two cohorts of students. First of all, I criticized this phenomenon for being too superficial. Then, I asked the students who identified with and engaged in the check-in to raise their hands, and they all did, which shocked me. Most of them were born in the 90s, with a small number born in the 80s. It can be concluded that checking in is a common hobby and cultural consumption feature of the new generation. Moreover, checking in has become an important and even primary purpose of travel for the vast majority of new-generation tourists. It has become increasingly common to visit a city just for the purpose of taking photos. Furthermore, the trend of checking in at popular attractions also deeply influences their parents and even grandparents, especially women.

3 Influencers should Engage in more Meaningful Activities than Just Checking in

I firmly hold that influencers should engage in more meaningful activities than just checking in, though this is a trend. Let's take a look at influencers' check-in process. First, influencers create a hot destination. Then, other influencers follow suit to visit the destination personally. Finally, numerous photos and video texts are shared on WeChat Moments and other social media platforms, creating a viral sensation. What are the characteristics of the check-in? First, we should recognize the influence of mobile Internet influencers. Second, due to the herd mentality, people are inclined to follow trends. Third, individuals tend to share photos on WeChat Moments to show off. Fourth, the younger generation has a higher demand for aesthetics than their parents and grandparents and even has a tendency toward aestheticism. Fifth, people focus more on outward appearances than on internal values. Sixth, influencers struggle to maintain enduring popularity. All influencers might become invisible or even be completely forgotten in a very short time, which is a typical characteristic of fast food culture. We need to find ways to guide this phenomenon. However, we cannot simply blame the younger generation. Instead, as the guardians of traditional culture, the elders should reflect on: Why do their words fail to resonate with the new generation? Why doesn't our education system work effectively?

4 Exploring and Highlighting the Cultural Value of Internet-famous Sites

The Guinness Storehouse in Dublin, the capital of Ireland, is an internationally renowned destination. In addition to offering beer and numerous popular facilities, the museum also subtly showcases its cultural values to tourists. The most impressive things about the museum are the two photos shown in Fig. 1. The photo on the right shows a franchise contract. The brewery was originally part of the government's public property. The contract was signed around the 45th year during the reign of Emperor Qianlong. The government decided to entrust its operations to Guinness, a private company, due to ineffective official management. The contract term was set for 9,000 years and remains in effect to this day. The photo on the left shows this contract placed underneath the floor glass in the public area of the museum. The value that the Irish people seek to convey is their commitment to contracts and the principle of integrity between governments and enterprises. Guinness has successfully linked a popular attraction with the dissemination of cultural values, a strategy that China's internet-famous sites can learn from.

Fig. 1 Cultural value display model of the Guinness Storehouse in Dublin

Westminster Abbey is a key attraction to convey cultural values in the United Kingdom. How does it convey these cultural values as an internationally renowned site? It promotes cultural values through the licensed tour guide system. There are two models for domestic tour guides. The first model allows tour guides or docents from various companies to access scenic spots without any restrictions. This will greatly diminish the professionalism, cultural depth, and value conveyed in the explanation. The second model is adopted in solemn scenic spots that promote mainstream values, such as revolutionary tourism scenic spots. These scenic spots allow only their designated docents to provide explanations. This model doesn't leverage high-quality explanation resources available in society. Furthermore, official guides are limited in number, covering only a small fraction of tourists. As a result, the majority of tourists end up exploring the sites without any guidance.

The United Kingdom has implemented an examination system where all individuals, including legally resident foreigners, can serve as guides for Westminster Abbey after passing the examination and obtaining a qualification certificate. This integrates market demand, market resources, and government management. I had the opportunity to hear the explanation of a licensed docent from Taiwan, China, who lives permanently in the United Kingdom. His explanation was exceptionally professional. After hearing his explanation, I suddenly understood why the United Kingdom was revered as "the empire on which the sun never sets". The history of the Kingdom of Great Britain can be thoroughly decoded in this church, largely due to its high level of explanations.

There are two online comments on the Wukang Building in Shanghai. The first comment, "Just wandering around, eating desserts, and drinking coffee here", is from a young man from outside Shanghai. It is hard to gauge the cultural value it conveys. The second comment was made by a cultural worker on Zhihu, stating, "I still expect tourist attractions to offer more than just queuing up for check-in". I share a similar sentiment. We seek the profound historical and spatial significance these sites embody.

The Wukang Building should have the potential to explore and present humanistic values. The following are my personal suggestions and experiences. First, the lifestyle of tenants in the Wukang Building, along with the community governance model, serves as a model in Shanghai. The overall quality of life in the community is relatively high. The Shanghai-based writer Chen Danyan has written a book on oral history that captures the lives of residents in the Wukang Building. Why should I stress this issue in particular? First, in addition to visiting attractions such as the Great Wall and the Palace Museum, foreigners traveling in China also need to experience the daily life of Chinese people, which is not emphasized by China's tourism industry. We often visit popular destinations but don't take the time to understand the lives of people in those countries. The Wukang Building offers Western tourists the best opportunity to understand Shanghai. Shanghai China International Travel Service Ltd. once launched a tourism product called "Be a Shanghainese for a Day", which finds its ideal setting at the Wukang Building. Currently, our inbound tourism is at the lowest level since China's reform and opening up and it urgently needs revitalization. The Wukang Building plays a significant role in this effort. Second, I believe the Wukang Building offers tourists an exceptional opportunity to gain insights into Shanghai. It stands as a primary landmark of Shanghai-style culture. This place perfectly reflects the essence of Shanghai. The Wukang Building itself is a multi-cultural melting pot, integrating British, French, and Central European architectural styles. Over various historical periods, the residents have integrated into a diverse community culture, exemplifying the essence of Shanghai-style culture. To understand Shanghai and China's reform and opening up, please visit the Wukang Building. Third, there is a unique cultural group in Shanghai known as "old clerks", which has never been heard of in Beijing or Guangzhou. What is the biggest characteristic of this group? This group is the personification of Shanghai-style culture. At the Peace Hotel, the senior jazz performances stand as one of the most iconic features of Shanghai culture in the world. Can the Wukang Building effectively mobilize the resources of "old clerks"? Is it feasible for them to serve as special-grade volunteer guides? The

Wukang Building, built in 1924, will celebrate its 100th anniversary next year. Will Xuhui District do something special for this notable occasion? For example, the district may hold a concert or an exhibition, which will be more appealing than many other activities because these activities are deeply embedded in the cultural fabric and heritage of our city.

Many active influencers focus on the theme of the Wukang Building, but many of them seek to utilize its popularity to boost their user traffic. It's also worth considering how to effectively utilize these influencers' resources and guide them. The Wukang Building fully aligns with the theme of World Cities Day. Can it develop some plans combined with this event? However, there is no need for all internet-famous sites to emphasize culture and value. Their popularity among the new generation is valuable in itself.

5 Increasing the Popularity of Classic Cultural Scenes

The Palace Museum has done well in this regard. The coffee and lipsticks it has released are extremely popular. At peak times, up to 80,000 lipsticks can be sold up in a single day. There are many reasons behind the popularity of these products, but the most important factor is effective planning. Without Dean Shan, would the Palace Museum have garnered such high popularity at that time? It is hard to say. There are many talented people in Shanghai, and the key lies in effectively identifying and maximizing their potential.

In summary, it is essential to integrate internet-famous site check-in with cultural classics.

Value Realization of Historical Building Preservation and Utilization

Xu Jinliang

Professor-level Senior Engineer, Distinguished Researcher Fellow at the Key Laboratory of Urban and Architectural Heritage Conservation (Southeast University), Ministry of Education, China, and Distinguished Researcher Fellow at the China-Portugal Joint Laboratory of Cultural Heritage Conservation Science Supported by the Belt and Road Initiative, Soochow University

This is an excerpt from the author's speech at the Shikumen Urban Regeneration Forum.

"We must attach importance to the efforts in keeping our history and culture alive and strong to preserve our roots for the survival and thriving of the Chinese ethos", General Secretary Xi Jinping proposed. Water flows continuously because it has a source, and trees thrive because they have roots. "Historical and cultural heritage is a valuable resource that is neither renewable nor replaceable, and its protection should always be given top priority. Only by preserving it in the present can we ensure its successful inheritance and development in the future". The old lanes in Shanghai are typically characterized by Shikumen buildings. Shikumen is a unique style of architecture that combines Western cultural influences with traditional Chinese residential features. It represents a distinctive type of residential housing in Shanghai and deserves to be preserved and passed on. However, the residents who have been living in these old Shikumen lanes for many years have their own sentiments and feelings about them. In the 1990s, there was a widespread demand for improving the living conditions of traditional old houses. However, traditional old houses faced significant challenges such as poor building quality, inadequate infrastructure, small living spaces, and complex living environments. Urban managers were faced with two choices: developing new residential communities on the outskirts of the city or demolishing old houses and constructing high-rise buildings. During the 1990s, people generally preferred to stay in the central urban areas, and there was a popular saying in Shanghai at that time: "I would rather have a bed in Puxi than have a room in Pudong." Generally speaking, traditional old houses are usually located in prime areas with well-developed supporting facilities for transportation, education, and healthcare. The choice made by urban managers is often based on economic considerations. Demolishing old houses and constructing high-rise buildings allows for the efficient utilization of existing infrastructure and public facilities, making it the most cost-effective option in terms of financial viability. Therefore, during the 1990s, this line of thinking prevailed across the country, leading to the widespread demolition of numerous traditional old buildings. The old urban areas were transformed with the construction of high-rise buildings, which did indeed improve infrastructure and the urban environment at that time, maximizing land utilization efficiency.

However, starting in 2000, experts began advocating for the preservation of ancient cities and the protection of historical contexts. Simultaneously, with changes in land supply policies, urban managers started shifting their focus to new urban areas outside the city. Developing new urban areas became fashionable as they did not have to deal with historical issues. Consequently, the old urban areas were neglected and fell victim to "urban maladies", manifested by the hollowing out of industries, an increase in the population of the economically disadvantaged, elderly, and migrants, outdated infrastructure, and susceptibility to traffic congestion and flooding. These problems persist to this day. In the 2019 Central Economic Work Conference, the concept of "urban renewal" was officially introduced for the first time. It emphasized the need to revitalize old urban areas and houses and address their "urban maladies" to achieve the goals of a "sponge city" and a "resilient city". In recent years, urban renewal has become increasingly popular. Here are six main targets of urban renewal:

1. Old residential communities, urban villages, and scattered housing;

2. Old commercial and office complexes;

3. Old factory buildings. Due to their prime areas, flexible architectural structures, and ample architectural space, in recent years, many old factory buildings in old urban areas have become scarce resources and priority targets for urban renewal, such as Beijing 798 and Chongqing Eling Testbed 2.

4. Old public facility buildings. In the past, there was a requirement to construct public facilities such as sports arenas and badminton courts at the township level. However, many of these facilities now remain vacant.

5. Historic buildings and areas are a key focus of urban renewal;

6. Urban fringe areas.

In response to these urban renewal targets, according to the requirements outlined in the *Notice on Preventing Major Demolition and Construction in the Implementation of Urban Renewal Action* of the Ministry of Housing and Urban-Rural Development of the People's Republic of China in 2021, four key approaches are emphasized: preservation, renovation, demolition, and rental. Urban managers used to have the habit of demolishing buildings, but now there is a requirement to prohibit major demolition and construction. The document strictly stipulates that "in principle, the area of demolished buildings within an urban renewal unit or project should not exceed 20% of the total existing floor area". Therefore, most traditional buildings need to be preserved and renovated, and their utilization should be done rationally. This demands a shift in the mindset of urban managers. Regarding specific historic buildings, especially cultural-relic buildings, in 2018, the General Office of the CPC Central Committee and the General Office of the State Council issued the *Several Opinions on Strengthen-*

ing the Reform of Protection and Utilization of Cultural Relics, which called for promoting the rational utilization of cultural relics. The preservation community has always emphasized the preservation of cultural-relic buildings. However, a related issue is the problem of vacancy or inefficient utilization. During my visit to a cultural-relic building protected at the municipal level in the ancient village of Xishan Island in Taihu Lake in 2021, I learned that the government had invested a huge amount of money in its restoration in 2009. However, it remained vacant and unused for over a decade, and there was uncertainty about how to utilize it. The local government official informed me that after 10 years of restoration, the building would require further repairs. Due to prolonged disuse, some components needed refurbishment, which is a characteristic of traditional Chinese timber structures—if they are not used, they deteriorate. Therefore, there has been an increasing emphasis on "adaptive reuse" in recent years.

The documents from the General Office of the CPC Central Committee and the General Office of the State Council in 2018 introduced several new requirements. First, it emphasized the need for rational utilization and promotion of utilization. Second, it called for social participation. Third, it highlighted the asset management of cultural relics resources. This represents a gradual process of transition, moving from preservation to utilization, from government-led initiatives to social participation, and from the traditional displaying concept of the preservation of cultural relics resources to the asset management of cultural relics resources. This shift in thinking is a significant development in the preservation community.

The utilization of historic buildings involves determining who will use them, how they will be used, and what constitutes utilization. Utilization refers to the behavior of displaying and using these functions to bring about social or economic benefits under certain preservation principles. The utilization of historic buildings is primarily divided into two categories. The first is "display use". Buildings are restored and mainly used as museums or other display spaces. Suzhou has invested a significant amount of money in the restoration of numerous historic buildings, some of which are located in excellent geographical areas and now serve as museums. For example, the "Ligeng Hall" on Pingjiang Road in Suzhou has been converted into the "Suzhou Urban Construction Museum". It's not that museums themselves are problematic, but when viewed from the perspective of activating cultural relics assets, museums can indeed preserve buildings but face challenges in attracting visitors. In Suzhou, for instance, various small-scale museums are abundant, many of which house state-owned cultural relics assets. However, the reality is that these museums often struggle with low visitor numbers. During my visit, I had conversations with museum staff, and their expressions of concern were truly disheartening. The display utilization is certainly important for historic buildings. However, when it comes to the numerous and diverse historic buildings in general, display utilization is more applicable for significant ancient buildings or historic buildings located in marginalized areas. For the majority of historic buildings, functional utilization is preferred, which involves either continuing their original functions or adapting them for new purposes.

There are two typical cases of "functional utilization". One typical case is the Xintiandi model. The Xintiandi model involves preserving and restoring historic buildings to create a commercial service center. The funds are balanced by developing residential projects on surrounding land plots. After the success of the Shanghai Xintiandi, Shui On Land replicated the model in other cities like Wuhan and Chongqing, achieving positive social and economic benefits. However, when they attempted to implement the model in Foshan, Guangdong, they encountered difficulties. The developer explained to me that Foshan's small urban size made it challenging to balance the "Lingnan Tiandi" historic block redevelopment project with surrounding residential developments. As a result, Shui On Land returned to Shanghai and successfully created the redeveloped block "Hong Shou Fang". Now they are working to upgrade the Zhaojialou Ancient Town, creating a new redevelopment project. This represents a historic building redevelopment model where the central historic area is preserved and transformed while residential developments are undertaken in the surrounding areas. Are all cases of social capital investment in historic area redevelopment successful? No. For example, after the completion of the first phase of the Yangzhou Jiaochang project, there was no further progress due to a lack of funds from surrounding projects to balance the investment or due to poor management. This serves as a clear example of both successful and unsuccessful cases (Fig. 1).

Shanghai Xintiandi   Yangzhou Jiaochang

Fig. 1 Typical cases
Note: The pictures come from the Internet.

The second case is Shanghai Tianzifang (Fig. 2). The renovation and utilization of the Tianzifang area are quite distinctive. It was not initially driven by any unit but rather emerged as a grassroots movement. Mr. Chen Yifei and artists like Er Dongqiang were among the first to open studios in Tianzifang. They renovated the old shikumen buildings, attracting many other artists to settle in the area. Over time, it gradually evolved into an art and creative display area, which is a phenomenon more commonly seen in Europe. Therefore, the local government began investing in improving infrastructure, aiming to create an exemplary self-renovated historic area. This area quickly gained popularity in China. Unfortunately, the development of

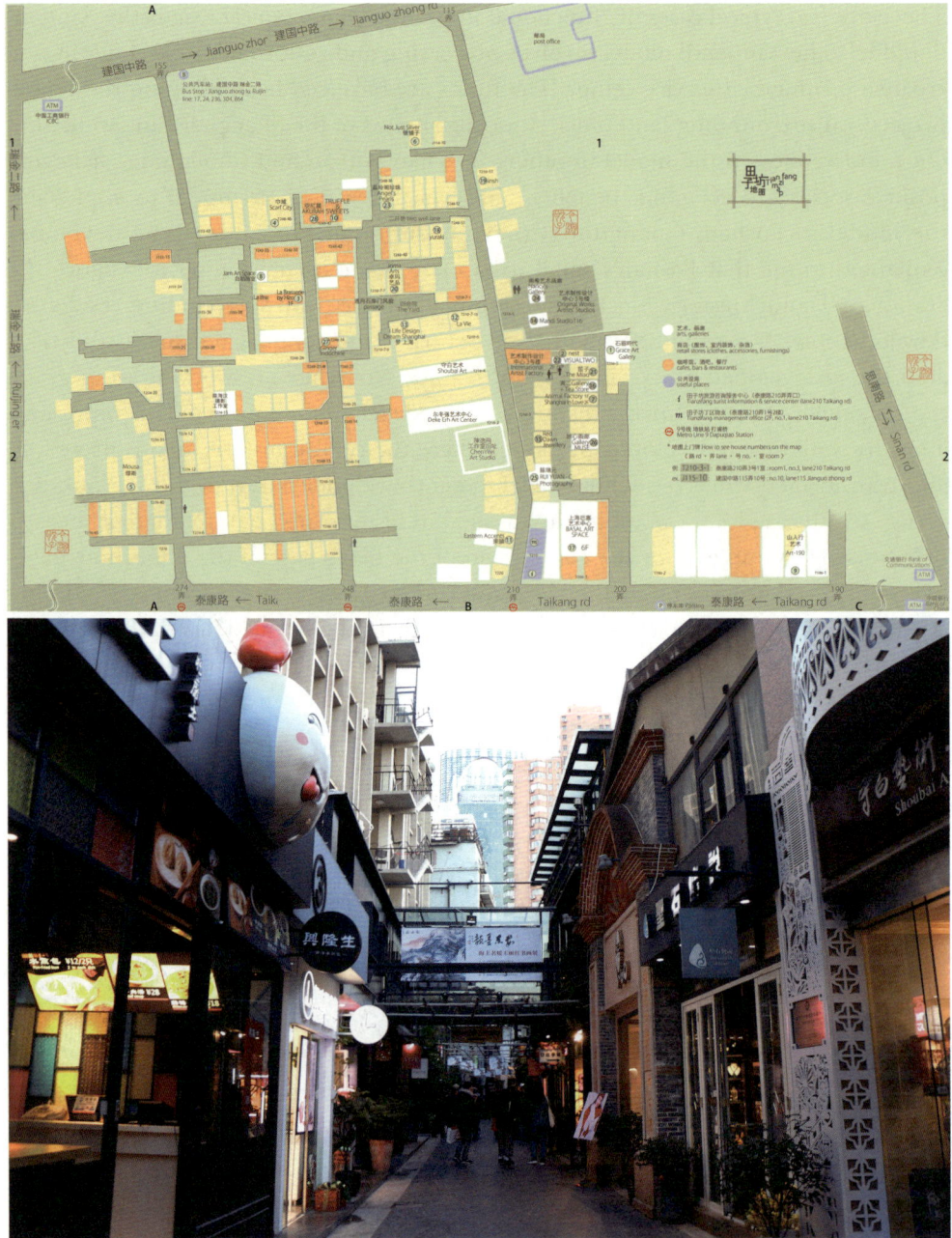

Fig. 2 Shanghai Tianzifang

the historic area encounters property rights issues. People are driven by profit, and in the case of Tianzifang, landlords began increasing rents, making it unaffordable for artists to stay. As a result, many art studios were transformed into leisure cafes. At first glance, it may appear that the historic block business district has become a bustling commercial area. However, the original soul of Tianzifang has been lost, and the unique artistic and cultural atmosphere that once made it stand out in Shanghai has disappeared. It has transformed into an ordinary historic tourist block, and gradually, the number of visitors has decreased, causing Tianzifang to fade from prominence.

This case prompts us to reflect on what the government should do in such situations. If the government could have promptly developed a preservation and development plan for the block, established a positive and negative list of industries, provided incentives and guidance for cultural and artistic industries, and imposed appropriate restrictions on property rentals, rather than letting the market drift aimlessly, it is entirely possible to preserve the original character of Tianzifang. "Macro-control and micro-incentives" are also necessary means to promote the rational utilization of historic buildings and historic areas.

Therefore, "functional utilization" must consider two aspects: social benefits (social value) and economic benefits (economic value). Display utilization may not need to prioritize monetary gains, but historic building preservation cannot solely rely on government investment, as it poses a practical challenge. For social capital, the potential for capital return is a consideration. At the very least, a basic balance or the generation of other social benefits is expected. Some social entities have expressed to me that investing in historic building renovations doesn't necessarily have to be profitable; it can serve as a show house. However, self-balance is essential; it cannot always be about pouring money into it. Ultimately, it boils down to finding a balance between social value and economic value.

Let us reassess the value of historic buildings. The field of heritage preservation has a comprehensive value system and value evaluation methods. According to the *Principles for the Conservation of Heritage Sites in China (2015)*, the value system for cultural relics is clearly defined as "five plus one": historical, artistic, scientific, social, and cultural value. Additionally, the principles also mention environmental factors (environmental value). Therefore, the preservation community often uses the concept of "six values" to elaborate on the value system.

How to perceive the historical value of historic buildings? Taking an antique as an example, a chicken cup from the Ming Dynasty (Pic. 3) was sold for RMB 120 million in 2012. First of all, how do historians interpret the chicken cup from the Ming Dynasty? They would analyze the physical shape of cups used among literati circles during the mid-Ming Dynasty, providing insights into the preferences and lifestyles of literati at that time. The physical existence and preserved features of the chicken cup provide valuable information for historians, thus giving it historical value. Art

Pic. 3 Chicken Cup from the Ming Dynasty
Note: The pictures come from the Internet.

researchers would interpret the aesthetic appeal of literati during that era from the cup. Scientific and technological personnel, on the other hand, would focus on the glaze used on the cup, the porcelain firing techniques employed, and the specific kiln responsible for its production. This is why professional technicians prefer to study actual artifacts. This showcases the scientific value of cultural relics.

Therefore, value, to some extent, is not a material existence. In philosophical theory, value refers to the interpretation and understanding of a material by the human subject. Moreover, information perception and value recognition can vary with changing times. Value recognition is the human subject's interpretation of the characteristic information contained in cultural relics, including historical and artistic information. Such characteristic information is carried by the physical carriers, which is why the core of the inheritance of historic buildings lies in their characteristic information, which is a material existence. The process by which the human subject interprets characteristic information leads to value recognition. While values can change, once the information is destroyed, it becomes irretrievable. Therefore, when historic buildings are demolished and rebuilt, they may appear similar to the original, but their essence undergoes actual changes, and the authentic and complete information they carry will be destroyed. That's why the preservation community emphasizes "authenticity" and "completeness", as they pertain to the inheritance of characteristic information. The carriers of information are the very essence of historic buildings, and they too require preservation and inheritance. Indeed, the key aspect of the inheritance of the chicken cup from the Ming Dynasty is to preserve the original artifact intact. That's why in 2021, the General Office of the CPC Central Committee and the General Office of the State Council issued the *Opinion on Strengthening the Protection and Inheritance of Historic and Cultural Heritage in the Course of Urban-Rural Development*. This document emphasizes the recognition of historical preservation and inheritance, aiming to shift the focus from mere preservation to the broader concept of the inheritance of history and culture. It represents a significant shift in conceptualization.

Compared to historic buildings, the characteristic information inherited by cultural relics and antiques is similar. However, there is one aspect that usually doesn't apply to cultural relics and antiques, and that is the "spatial attribute". After all, historic buildings are fundamentally real estate and are designed for specific spatial purposes. Owners typically wouldn't directly use a chicken cup from the Ming Dynasty that was purchased for RMB 120 million to drink tea, let alone use it to entertain guests. However, historic buildings need to utilize their space for reception, socializing, dining, accommodation, and more. Additionally, the location of the historic building, the preservation of surrounding historic areas, and the harmony between the historic building and its environment are also crucial considerations. The spatial attribute is specifically manifested in two aspects: one is the internal space, and the other is the environmental attribute. These determine the use function and availability and have an impact on the cultural value and social influence of the historic building.

According to the definition provided in *Cihai* (a large-scale dictionary and encyclopedia of Standard Mandarin Chinese), the concept of "value" encompasses two attributes. The first attribute is the traditional understanding of value, which refers to the characteristics of being good or bad, advantageous or disadvantageous, feasible or unfeasible that individuals assign to objects or things relevant to their lives based on their needs, desires, interests, or purposes. The second attribute is economic value. In analyzing the categories of commodities, value, and labor, Karl Marx pointed out that "As exchange-values, all commodities are merely definite quantities of congealed labor-time". Therefore, the understanding of value in *Cihai* encompasses two systems: the philosophical value system and the economic value system. Currently, cultural relics departments or architectural heritage departments tend to focus on the philosophical value system in their recognition of value. The purpose of the evaluation is to determine the quality of the heritage, with those scoring higher being prioritized for recognition as cultural relics, and those scoring even higher being designated as various levels of protected cultural relics. From an economic perspective, value is the economic value measured in terms of currency. The existence of economic value is determined by three important factors: utility, scarcity, and people's desire, ability, and willingness to occupy and use property, as well as other factors related to the process of exchange of ownership or possession.

What is the relationship between the traditional value and economic value of historic buildings? Some scholars attribute economic value to social value. Specifically, historic buildings themselves are individual material entities, encompassing two material existence. The first is the characteristic information, which gives rise to the recognition of historical value, scientific value, socio-cultural value, and other multi-angle, multidimensional, multi-level, dynamic values. The second is the spatial attribute, which leads to the use value (usability). Although the foundations and mechanisms of value formation differ, when these values enter human society, they generate social benefits, namely utility and efficiency. When something possesses utility, desire, scarcity, and effective purchasing power, it acquires economic value (Fig. 4 and Fig. 5). Therefore, the traditional value of historic buildings is an intrinsic value. Once its carrier enters the economic market, it forms an extrinsic economic value. The two are in an intrinsic-extrinsic relationship, not an inclusive relationship. Economic value is not a part of the traditional value of historic buildings; rather, it represents how much money the historic buildings are worth when they enter the economic market. We need to learn to analyze and view the preservation and utilization of historic buildings from an economic perspective: how to pass on and preserve them and how to distribute benefits. Economic benefits are now an unavoidable issue in the investment for the preservation and utilization of historic buildings.

Fig. 4   Elements of economic value formation

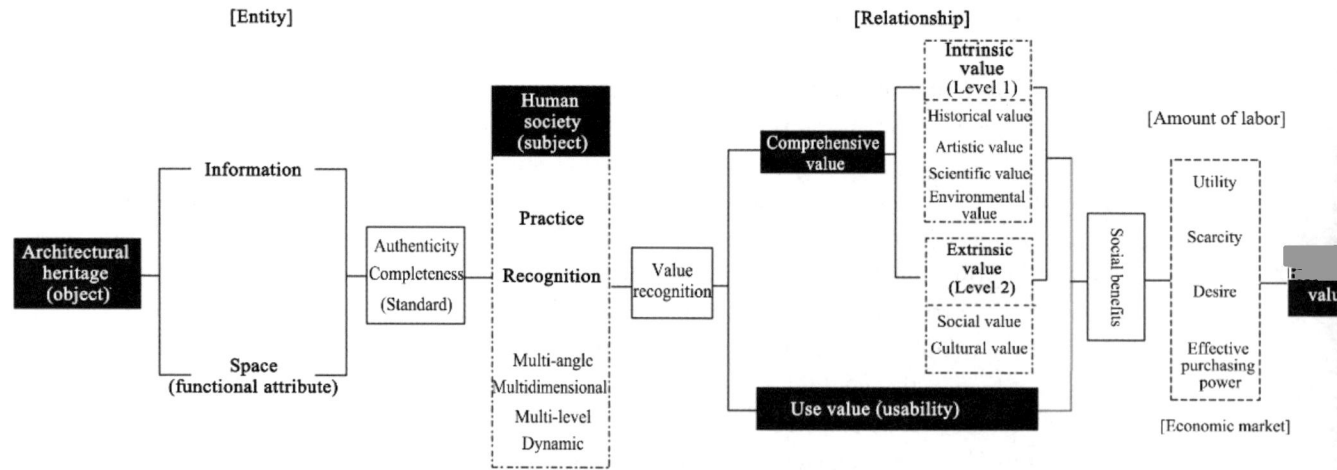

Fig. 5　Value system of historic buildings

Economics is not about studying how much money one can earn or the monetary value of something. Economic analysis is a perspective, a way of thinking. Its primary purpose is to guide and regulate human behavior. Since individuals are different from one another, each individual naturally seeks to maximize their own interests. However, at the societal and collective levels, there must be a balance. Achieving this balance requires the establishment of rules, and property rights are fundamental rules in economic society. Therefore, the first step in economic analysis is to understand property rights. Clear property rights are necessary for resource allocation, coordination of transaction costs, and ultimately, the efficient utilization of scarce resources. In practical terms, we introduce economics to accomplish two tasks: one is to guide the establishment of a set of effective behavioral rules, and the other is to establish asset management of cultural relics resources. Asset management itself falls under economic behavior. Asset management involves three key elements: resources, assets, and capital. Resources embody the physical entity itself; assets represent the property rights relationship and the potential revenue model. Assets are not about making money; the core is to clarify property rights. Capital, on the other hand, involves the source of funds and the revenue distribution model. Therefore, the logical relationship among resources, assets, and capital is progressively interconnected (Fig. 6). The original viewpoint was that cultural relics cannot be commodified, as their utilization would lead to destruction. However, this perspective has gradually shifted. The asset stage involves property rights rules and revenue models, while the capital stage gradually introduces social capital based on the clarity of property rights. When it comes to introducing capital and assessing whether it is worth investing, a quantifiable rule is needed, namely the evaluation of economic value.

The demolition of the historic building at 888 Julu Road, Shanghai in 2017 caused a significant uproar. Eventually, the authorities ordered the restoration of the original state and imposed a RMB 30.5 million administrative penalty (Fig. 7). At the time, when studying the causes of this incident, we believed that the property owner had

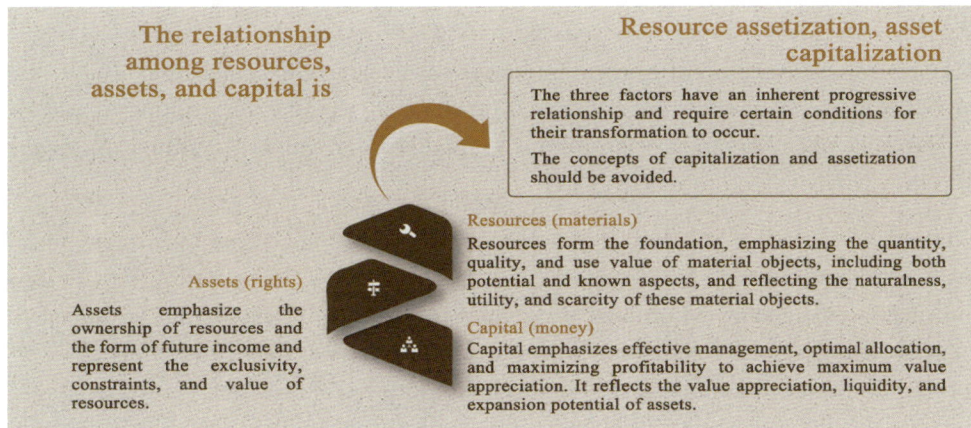

Fig. 6 Relationship diagram of resources, assets, and capital

Fig. 7 888 Julu Road, Shanghai
Note: The pictures come from the Internet.

not invested much during the initial purchase, indicating a lack of sufficient recognition of the economic value of the historic building. As a result, the owner did not attach much importance to its preservation. If the owner had purchased the historic building for RMB 100 million, he/she might have been less willing to demolish it. In fact, such situations frequently occur in urban development, and we need a set of rules to guide the market where demolition costs more than reconstruction. I personally have accomplished something I am proud of. There was a historic bridge in Anhui that was planned to be demolished for road construction. I evaluated the economic value and determined that the bridge was worth RMB 200 million. With this information, I persuaded the government to modify the plan and preserve the bridge and the surrounding architectural heritage. Therefore, sometimes communicating with urban managers using the language of economics can be more effective than relying solely on reasoning and heritage preservation and inheritance arguments.

How to quantify economic value? First, what makes historic buildings better or worse than ordinary buildings? We all know that historic buildings possess a special traditional value, including historical, artistic, and cultural values, which is why they can be designated as listed ancient buildings. Therefore, the traditional value is a special appreciation factor.

The use value (usability) of historic buildings varies from one to another due to the cost of repairs, maintenance conditions, and the state of past renovations, as well as the possibility of renovation or additions, so the economic value can either appreciate or depreciate because of the use value.

There is also another factor that can decrease the economic value of historic buildings. For listed ancient buildings, there must be specific preservation restrictions limiting building renovation and functional utilization. Therefore, it is crucial to clearly define property rights and communicate the associated constraints. It is essential to inform stakeholders about the limitations regarding renovation possibilities, use possibilities, permissible uses, and the required approval processes for renovation. Currently, there is a need for improvement in addressing this issue across different regions.

By clarifying the differences between historic buildings and ordinary buildings, we can identify the various special factors that affect their economic value appreciation or depreciation (Fig. 8). This provides a direction for the technical approach to their evaluation. It's worth noting that in 2024, the *Technical Guidelines for Historic Building Valuation* will be published by the China Institute of Real Estate Appraisers and Agents (CIREA), which is affiliated with the Ministry of Housing and Urban-Rural Development. The introduction of technical standards for evaluating the economic value of historic buildings provides urban managers, planners, investors, and users with a technical reference standard. This gradual standardization helps to visualize the economic value and better reflect the unique connotation of the traditional value of historic buildings.

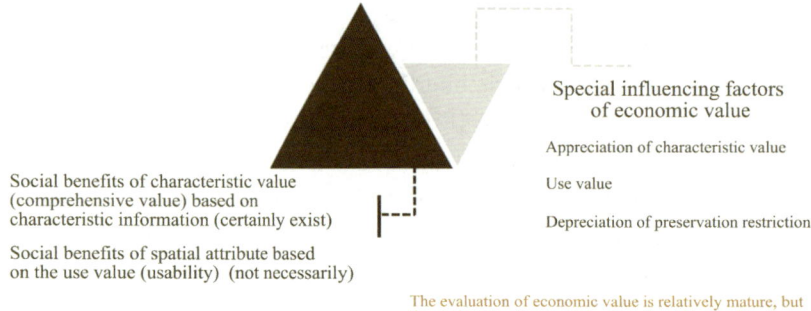

Fig. 8 Schematic diagram of special factors affecting the economic value of historic buildings

I would like to conclude with a quote from my mentor, Professor Zhu Guangya from the School of Architecture at Southeast University, "Whether it is planning, restoration, theory, technology, engineering, design, utilization, or evaluation, they are all tools and means, with the ultimate goal being heritage inheritance". Therefore, while today I have interpreted the preservation and utilization of historic buildings from the perspectives of traditional and economic values, the ultimate goal is to preserve, utilize, and pass on the historic buildings that our ancestors have left us.

Chapter V

Urban Renewal and Digital Empowerment

Shanghai Shikumen Lilong: Transformation Process and Regeneration Models[1]

CHANG Qing
Academician of the Chinese Academy of Sciences

This is an excerpt from the author's speech delivered at the Shikumen Urban Regeneration Forum.

1 Origin Exploration of Shikumen Lilong Residences

In the nearly 170 years since their emergence in the 1850s, Shikumen Lilong Residences in Shanghai characterized by townhouses with multiple courtyard units became globally famous for their adaptability in the interaction and fusion of Eastern and Western cultures.

Fig. 1 Shikumen Lilong Residences and urban grain of old Shanghai

According to statistical data, when the People's Republic of China was founded in 1949, Shanghai had only 93 high-rise buildings over 24 m tall. Among the city's built environment and urban grain, Shikumen Lilong Residences represented the largest share. Together with other types of lilong residences, they shaped the figure-ground relationship of Shanghai—an international metropolis in the Far East (Fig. 1). At that time, most urban residents lived in these areas. Therefore, Shikumen Lilong Res-

---

1 This paper is originally published in *Science China* in May 2023. It has been revised according to the Special Report from the Academician Symposium held at the Shanghai Science Hall on September 6, 2021. Foundation item: Key Project supported by the National Natural Science Foundation of China (51738008).

idences have been acknowledged as the primary carrier of Shanghai's urban memory and the foremost emblem of the city's identity.

1.1 Origin of terms

"Lilong" is also known as "fanglong", originating from the ancient word "lüli". It was formalized during the Tang Dynasty as "lifang", signifying divisions of land and residential units in the capital. In this context, "li" refers to the scale of living space, while "fang" indicates the area of residence. Lifang was originally a walled area within the city, housing markets inside its boundaries, with no open commercial streets outside. However, some cities did not always conform to this model. For instance, during the late Tang Dynasty, Yangzhou featured vibrant commercial streets known for their "markets stretching for miles" and "thousands of lights brightening the night sky". (Note 1) The Northern Song Dynasty marked the first transformation of "lifang" in the capital, Dongjing, into "xiangfang" or "jiefang".

The walls that once surrounded the fang were dismantled, allowing commercial streets to extend beyond this space—a change that has been carried forward by subsequent generations. The lilong residences in the Shanghai concession at the end of the Qing Dynasty embodied the cultural essence of the ancient jiefang or neighborhood.

"Li" in Shikumen Lilong Residences refers to the neighborhood enclosed by urban streets, while "long (lane)" denotes the alleys within that neighborhood, pronounced "xiang" or "long" in the fourth tone. There are main and branch lanes, "long" is generally known as "longtang", meaning the open space in front of a door. There is a widely held opinion about the origin of the term "shikumen". It proposes that the residential units in the "lilong" were framed with stone strips, leading to the name "shigumen" in the Ningbo dialect. As "gu" is pronounced similarly to "ku" in the local dialect, the term gradually transformed into "shikumen". Since "long (lane)" was originally written in a different form in early texts, it is reasonable to assume that "shikumen" should have a corresponding literary reference. "Kumen" refers to the second door in ancient palaces and storerooms (such as the five gates of a royal palace: gao, ku, zhi, ying, and lu). In this context, "shikumen" is the second door into the residential courtyard (with the first being the "longmen"), specifically describing a "kumen" framed with stone strips. The flourishing "Xiangshan group" in Suzhou during the Ming Dynasty produced a renowned manual for artisans titled *Basic Rules for Building* at the end of the Qing Dynasty and the beginning of the Republic of China. In this text, the entrance to Su-style courtyards, referred to as "qiangmen (wall door)", is called "kumen".[1] (Note 2) This indicates that the term "shikumen", meaning stone-framed door, indeed originates from the terminology used for residence doors in Jiangnan's traditional architecture. (Fig. 2)

Thus, the historical and cultural significance of the term "shikumen" has deep roots and continues to be relevant. Even when residence doors were later constructed using brick arches or a combination of brick and concrete with decorative plaster, they still retained the name "shikumen". These stone-framed doors are widely found in traditional residences across the Jiangnan region, especially in the Wuyue culture area, Anhui, and Jiangxi. While "shikumen" originates from "kumen", it does not solely

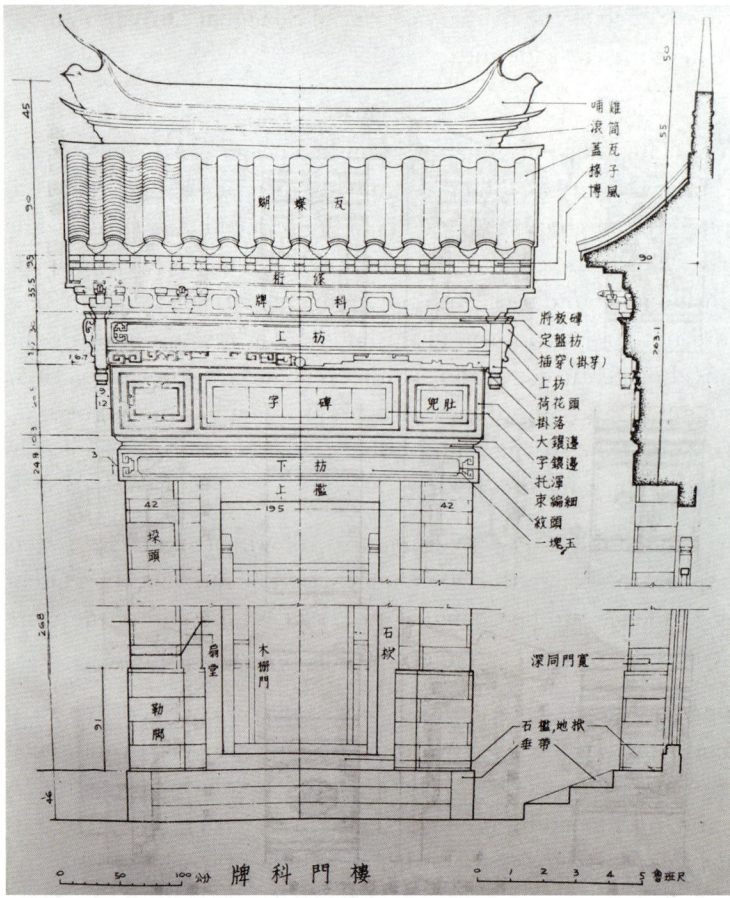

Fig. 2 Gatehouse of Suzhou-style residence: Qiangmen–kumen

Fig. 3 Western-style gatehouse of a new style shikumen building: Sidali, Lane 57, Shanyin Road, Shanghai

designate a residence or wall door. Instead, it serves as a general term for the accompanying buildings and neighborhoods. In a similar vein, "taimen" in Shaoxing, like "shikumen", does not refer to just one entrance but broadly encompasses a cluster of residences named after prominent local surnames. Analyzing from the standpoint of Western modern urban morphology theory, "shikumen" effectively represents a network of lilong matrix composed of streets, main lanes, and branch lanes that encircle the block. This network interacts with the artifacts within the block, such as shikumen buildings, structures, plants, and signage, collectively establishing a figure-ground relationship within the Shikumen Lilong Residences neighborhood. (Fig. 3)

1.2 Morphological transformation

Academic consensus generally categorizes Shanghai's lilong residences into five types: "early Shikumen Lilong Residences", "later Shikumen Lilong Residences", "new style lilong", "garden lilong", and "apartment lilong".[2] In the modern history of Shanghai, Shikumen Lilong Residences emerged in old Shanghai, closely linked to the intersection and interaction of Chinese and Western civilizations. This evolution transitioned from English-style bungalows to traditional Chinese townhouses and eventually led to those embodying a fusion of both cultures. For a century, this transition illustrates a significant process of morphological transformation and acculturation.

In 1843, British Consul C.G. Balfour rented a house with 52 rooms from the Gu family (transliterated) on Se Yaon Road in the old county town of Shanghai, which became the temporary residence of the consulate. In 1845, Circuit Intendant of Shanghai Gong Mujiu and Balfour signed the *Land Regulation* (Note 3), which implemented a policy of "segregation of Chinese and foreigners", stipulating that Chinese individuals were prohibited from renting houses built within designated areas. At that time, the British Concession spanned 55.33 ha. (830 *mu*), but it grew to 188 ha. (2,820 *mu*) just three years later. Within this area, there were only 175 foreigners, all residing in the village houses along the Huangpu River[3]. In 1853, during the Xiaodaohui Uprising, Shanghai was overtaken, resulting in a large number of people seeking shelter in the concessions. While it remains unclear whether temporary wooden huts were erected to meet the immediate housing demands, the *Land Regulation* explicitly prohibited the construction of fire-prone structures such as "thatched huts, bamboo houses, and wooden shacks".[4] (Note 4) Subsequent regulations also included similar prohibitions. Therefore, it is likely that simpler townhouses made of brick and wood, inspired by 18th and 19th-century Georgian and Victorian architecture from Britain, were constructed during this period instead. (Fig. 4)

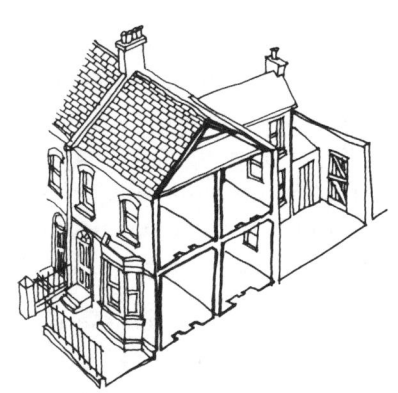

Fig. 4　British brick-timber townhouses in the early 20th century

The unrest from the wars opened up real estate opportunities in the concessions. As a result, the British Concession authorities teamed up with American and French Concession colonial officials the following year to revise the *Land Regulation*, allowing Chinese individuals to rent houses within the concessions. It is reasonable to conclude that Jiangnan vertical-style wooden frame townhouses likely became the preferred residences for Chinese individuals entering the concessions. The new regulation references "constructing houses, erecting wooden frames, and utilizing brick, tile, and wood materials", indicating a focus on brick-and-wood structures.[5] This type of structure includes firewalls between houses, which may help explain the early Chinese origins of the Shikumen Lilong Residences. Moreover, the *Land Regulation* established strict guidelines for urban order concerning public interests within the

Chapter V　Urban Renewal and Digital Empowerment

concessions. It prohibited activities such as cutting down trees, excavating soil for graves in other areas, encroaching on public roadways (historically referred to as "encroaching on the street" in China), extending eaves over public spaces, stacking items and garbage, discharging wastewater into the streets, and causing disturbances that could disrupt others. These fundamental rules set a precedent that influenced urban development and public management in modern Shanghai.

The early Shikumen Lilong Residences in Shanghai, commonly known as "old-style Shikumen Lilong Residences", likely emerged from traditional shikumen residences found in Jiangnan settlements (cities, towns, and villages). The earliest recorded example is Xingrenli in the British Concession, built in the mid-19th century (demolished in 1980). These residences typically featured floor plans with three to five rooms and followed traditional wooden frame construction (tenon through structures), characterized by dark tiles and white walls. Firewalls between houses and gable walls often displayed Hui-style horsehead walls or Wu-style Guanyin Crown walls. The stone door frames were topped with brick-built Chinese eaves, complemented by black lacquered wooden doors and brass door rings. Many interiors included a traditional courtyard layout, resulting in interconnected townhouse configurations that were likely influenced by the traditional street patterns in Laochengxiang of old Shanghai.

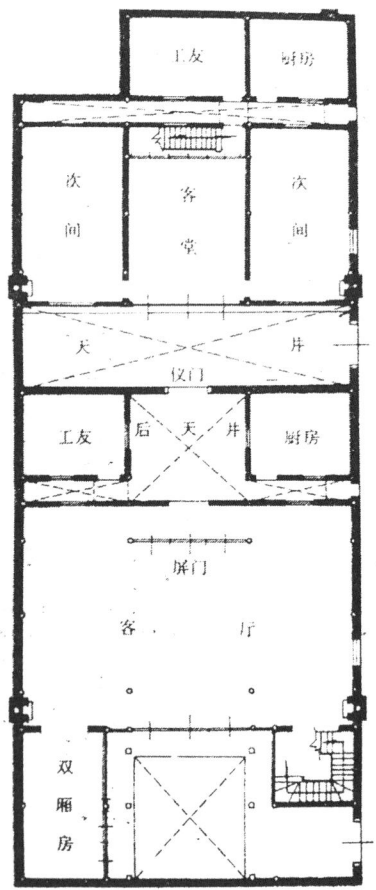

Fig.5 Plan of early Shikumen Lilong Residence Hongdeli

Due to their large footprint, minimal material usage, rapid deterioration, lack of standardization, and low construction efficiency, these old-style Shikumen Lilong Residences began to transition to newer styles in the early 20th century. Following various periods of demolition, renovation, and reconstruction, only a few examples, such as Hongdeli, have retained traces of traditional architecture.[6] (Fig. 5 and Fig. 6)

In the 1910s, Shanghai witnessed the rise of "late Shikumen Lilong Residences", predominantly influenced by Western architectural styles, commonly referred to as "new style Shikumen Lilong Residences". This trend culminated in the 1930s. These lilong residences are closely linked to the upgraded brick-and-timber townhouse designs from Britain in the early 20th century.[7] They utilized standardized unit-based construction methods that supported industrialized mass development. Its spatial layout combines characteristics of both traditional neighborhoods and Western-style blocks while retaining the intricate texture relationships typical of Chinese lilong. However, the architectural facades are uniform, and the longtang network is straight and unobstructed, position-

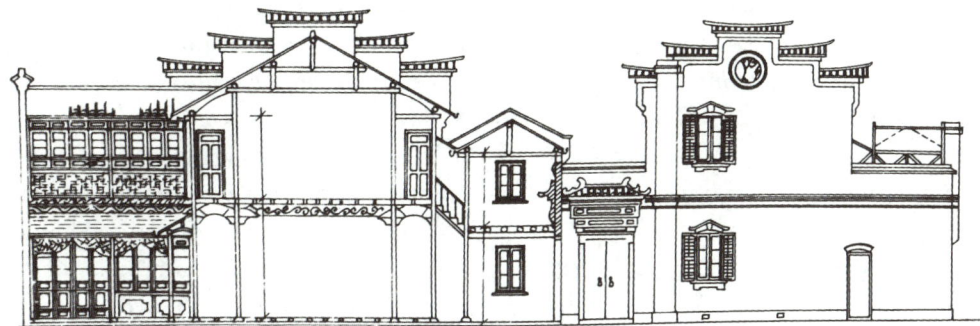

Fig.6　Profile of early Shikumen Lilong Residence Hongdeli

Fig.7　Aerial View of late Shikumen Lilong Residence Bugaoli

ing it among the leading residential districts in Far Eastern cities at that time. (Fig. 7 and Fig. 8)

A key feature of the new style Shikumen Lilong Residences is their larger scale and smaller unit sizes, typically one to two rooms. These houses primarily used Western-style brick-and-timber construction (with later examples incorporating brick-concrete methods), characterized

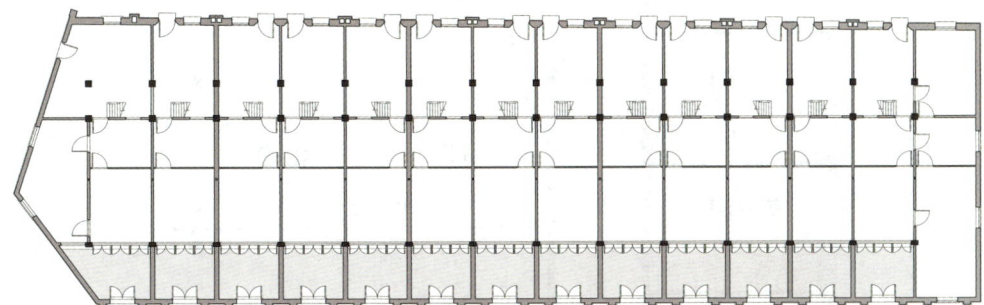

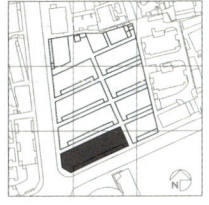

172～196号位置图

Fig.8　Plan of No. 172～196 at late Shikumen Lilong Residence Bugaoli

Chapter V Urban Renewal and Digital Empowerment

by triangular roof woodwork and load-bearing brick walls. They also include tiled roofs, red brick walls or black brick walls with red brick embellishment, pavilions, rear extensions, balconies, arched door and window openings, and triangular or round pediment or arch lintel with cartouch. This reflects a strong atmosphere of cultural fusion between Eastern and Western influences. (Fig. 9 –Fig. 11) By this time, the Chinese residents in the concessions had gradually come to accept these new-style shikumen residences. Even as Shanghai's "garden lilong" and "apartment lilong" absorbed Western architectural influences, the essence and architectural elements of the Jiangnan neighborhood remained distinctly present. Since the late 1980s, several academic works have explored the characteristics and evolution of Shikumen Lilong Residences.[8–12]

1.3 Situation and problems

In old Shanghai, the overcrowding was reflected in low-rise, high-density buildings. Statistics show that in 1949, the urban area of 82.4 km² accommodated 3 million residents. Over the past half-century, although downtown Shanghai has expanded to approximately eight times its original size, the population has only increased to around 10 million—more

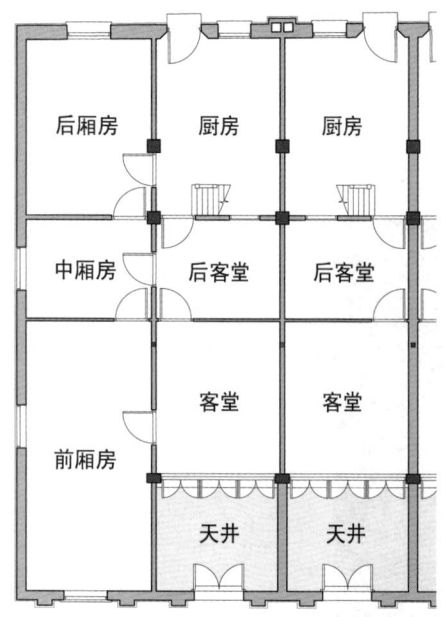

Fig. 9 Ground floor plan of Bugaoli (double room and single room)

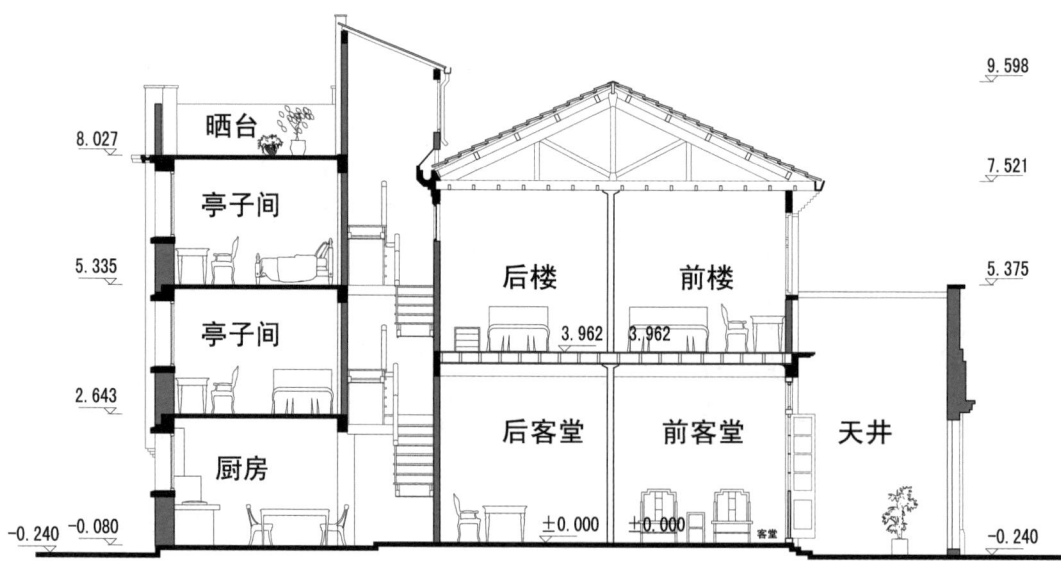

Fig. 10 Profile of No. 196 at late Shikumen Lilong Residence

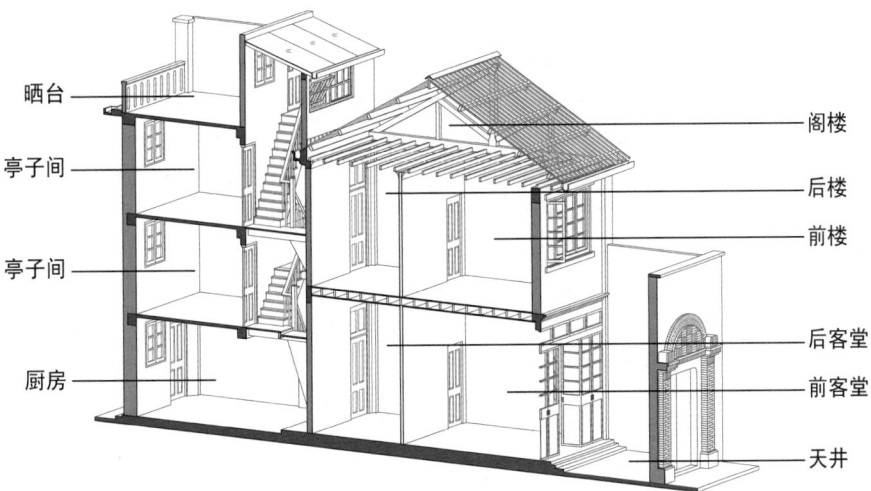

Fig. 11 Axonometric drawing of standard units in Bugaoli

than three times its previous number—resulting in a reduction in density of over 60% compared to the early years after the founding of the People's Republic of China. According to statistics from 1949-1950, there were 9,214 lilong lanes in Shanghai at that time, covering an area of 12.425 million m². More than two-thirds (about 2 million) of the urban population lived in these lanes. Among them, Shikumen Lilong Residences accounted for a large proportion.

After more than 70 years of significant changes, particularly the nearly 40 years of urban renewal—which included initiatives such as "house renovation", "demolition of illegal structures", and "relocation"—by the time of the Expo 2010 Shanghai China, the city had completed housing projects for 830,000 households, covering an area of 20.76 million m², about two-thirds of the total area designated for renovation in the old districts. By the second decade of the 21st century, the benefits of urban renewal had waned, and economic and social conditions had evolved significantly. The remaining 400,000 households and 8.74 million m² of low-quality housing have proven increasingly difficult to renovate. As a result, the process has been slow, with ongoing efforts to explore viable solutions.[13] In this evolving context, the future of the existing 8.13 million m² of lilong residences in Shanghai's urban area is uncertain and cannot be easily determined. The official guideline indicates that around 90% of these lilong residences, approximately 7.3 million m², will be preserved, renovated, or renewed. However, figuring out how to preserve and renew these structures poses considerable challenges.

2 Shikumen Lilong Residences and Built Heritage

2.1 Problems

Shikumen Lilong Residences broadly encompass a variety of housing types, including a few luxurious Western-style houses and mansions from the former upper class, modest courtyard townhouses for the working class, and a significant number of low-quality residences resembling slum-like communities, such as "Seventy-Two Households", which had long been known as "old neighborhoods below the second level". Typical Shikumen Lilong Residences have attained legal designation as units of cultural relic protection at various levels, historical and cultural zones, and significant historical buildings. However, Shanghai's historical practice of leasing land for real estate development, usually with lease periods of only 20 to 30 years, has led to low quality in Shikumen Lilong Residences. These residences suffer from high density, poor living conditions, and inadequate supporting facilities. The complexities of property ownership and residential rights, along with the challenges of cost-effective repairs and improvements, make it difficult to protect and renew these residences. Among these, buildings that lack a protected status or have an ambiguous status often have qualifying terms like "preserved", "general", or "heritage" added before the legal designation of "historical buildings". Given the extensive scope of this portion, it has been likened to a "chicken rib"—something that lacks substantial value yet is hard to get rid of. In the context of urban renewal, this creates a dilemma regarding whether to keep or remove these structures, placing considerable pressure and challenges on all stakeholders involved.

Therefore, when facing the challenges of urban renewal guided by the principles of "retainment", "renovation", and "demolition" (as well as the subsequent "reconstruction" after demolition) about old residential areas, it is crucial to determine how to effectively address these issues. This necessitates a reevaluation of the origins and dynamics of the shikumen issue from both epistemological and methodological perspectives, employing a comparative analysis of heritage discourse both domestically and internationally. The goal is to identify solutions that are appropriate for both national and local contexts. In light of this, the following discussion will begin by exploring "shikumen" and its associated heritage discourse.

2.2 Heritage discourse

"Built heritage" refers to cultural heritage created through construction, including architectural heritage, settlement heritage (including cities, towns, and villages), and landscape heritage. Shikumen Lilong Residences are both settlement heritage and architectural heritage. In the industrial era, built heritage primarily referred to monuments and sites. However, since the 1960s, when the West transitioned into a post-industrial society, there has been an increasing focus on cultural heritage. Firstly, the *Venice Charter* (Note 5) was adopted at the Second Congress of Architects and Specialists of Historic Buildings in 1964, establishing principles for the restoration of historic sites with global significance. The author has summarized this principle as "restoring the old as the old while adapting the new", essentially referring to "repair". It emphasizes the importance of preserving the original site and materials through the same methods used historically. For any "touch-up" work, it is crucial to differentiate the new from the old, leaving visible traces of the intervention.[14] The *Convention Concerning the Protection of the World Cultural and Natural Heritage* was adopted by UNESCO in 1972, significantly broadening the scope for recognizing and identifying built heritage. As material civilization advances, our desire for cultural memory and identity continues to grow. As a carrier of these sentiments, the built heritage has expanded from mere monuments to include all elements worthy of remembrance and nostalgia related to the past. Thus, the global phenomenon of heritage fever has emerged.[15] Renowned British historian David Lowenthal commented on this, stating that in our rapidly evolving technological and cultural era, everything that rises tends to fall; the past is a foreign country. In the fear of loss and change, tightly grasping the remaining willpower helps us respond in a calm and self-possessed manner. The willpower that he mentioned is heritage.[16]

Under the influence of this heritage fever, old buildings and historic neighborhoods that embody urban memory and tourism value have become targets for conservation. For example, in the historical conservation district of Lyon, France, structures ranging from Renaissance-era homes to 18th and 19th-century workers' housing in the Croix Rousse have become part of the world cultural heritage. (Fig. 12) Furthermore, the conservation-worthy sites have become "younger", as seen in the *New York City Charter* and *Administrative Code*, which considers buildings that are thirty years old or older and of good quality for conservation.[17] In the past fifty years, especially after the Shanghai Municipal People's Government promulgated the *Regulations of Shanghai Municipality on the Protection of Historical-feature Areas and Excellent Historical Buildings* 20 years ago, a vast conservation system has developed for legally recognized built heritage and policy-preserved objects of all levels and types in Shanghai, including Shikumen Lilong Residences. Moreover, buildings over 50 years old must undergo individual characteristic identification and value assessment, and cannot be arbitrarily demolished. This aligns closely with international heritage discourse and values.[18] (Note 6)

Fig. 12 Exterior of 18th and 19th-century workers' housing in Croix Rousse

2.3 Intervention methods

It is undeniable that all conservation targets have their life cycles, which leads to the question of whether to allow them to deteriorate or to invest in periodic maintenance and restoration based on monument conservation principles, enabling them to live on and achieve regeneration in some manner. The ongoing international debate regarding value and intervention over the past two centuries cannot be simply applied to the vast number of conservation targets today, as the rarity of heritage is no longer a compatible perspective. Today, the rationale for heritage recognition is increasingly diverse, often overlooking how this broad range of recognized heritage integrates into contemporary and future life. The 18th-century British philosopher David Hume noted that the diversity of object values is ingrained in the variety of ideas of the one who perceives the objects, rather than the characteristics of the objects themselves. Similarly, Lowenthal argued that the relationship between heritage and the present is a human construct rather than a result of natural causation. Consequently, historical conservation should not be isolated from the evolution of society but should become an urbanistic impulse and a means of cautiously shaping culture in modern society.[19] The 1977 *Charter of Machu Picchu*, which had a profound impact on the international architecture and planning community, proposed regeneration pathways that balance heritage value and vitality. To ensure that heritage carries economic value and truly thrives, conservation and construction must advance in tandem, adapting to the urbanization process and facilitating coexistence between the old and the new.[20]

The term "intervention methods" refers to the various technical means and practical methods for the conservation and revitalization of built heritage. Broadly speaking, intervention involves three fundamental concepts and their application scopes.

First, conservation refers to managing change rather than simply freezing evolution. Whether as historical specimens or as objects that can undergo partial renewal, conservation necessitates moderate intervention methods, including preservation, restoration, renovation, addition, and anastylosis or reconstruction. Shikumen Lilong Residences should employ different or integrated conservation intervention methods based on their significance and protection categories. From this perspective, the greatest significance of heritage protection lies in mastering the ability to realistically reproduce it.

Second, regeneration in Chinese literally means "repair old things for new uses", referring to comprehensive interventions for repairing, refurbishing, and reusing or revitalizing remaining or abandoned conservation targets. "Sorting out the national heritage and recreating civilization", as stated by Hu Shi, encapsulates a broader sense of regeneration.[21] Therefore, conservation is a prerequisite for regeneration, while regeneration serves as the goal of conservation.

Third, renewal, generally implying "removing the old to build the new", can apply to the transformation of old districts and improving urban quality. However, regarding built heritage and its historical environments, one must be cautious of drastic transformation and renewal practices caused by improper control measures, especially the large-scale demolition and construction that could cause cultural amnesia and disrupt the cycle of reuse. Excessive intervention termed "urban renewal" has already occurred on a large scale in the historical city renewal context in China, as demonstrated by cases where some historical cultural districts disappeared entirely in famous historical and cultural cities.

3 Regeneration Models of Shikumen Lilong Residences

In 2002, Shanghai issued the *Regulations of Shanghai Municipality on the Protection of Historical-feature Areas and Excellent Historical Buildings*, which considers international built heritage conservation concepts, experience, and the relevant national laws and regulations. The detailed implementation rules take into account the linkage between identity attributes and conservation levels. For Class I excellent historical buildings, the control measures resemble those of cultural relics protection; for Classes II and III, different levels of enhancements and modifications are allowed, thus allowing for greater intervention; while for Class IV, only retaining a main facade is required, and the rest can be renovated or renewed as needed. (Fig. 13) Regarding the many subpar iconic buildings within historical feature areas, there is a lack of consensus among stakeholders on how to regenerate these buildings, leaving them caught in a dilemma of preservation versus demolition.[22] Up until now, the conservation and regeneration modes applicable to Shanghai's Shikumen Lilong Residences can broadly be divided into four types.[23] (Note 7)

Fig. 13 Aerial view of Xiafei Fang (Huaihai Fang)

3.1 Model of cultural relics protection

The mode focuses primarily on specimen conservation. This includes Shikumen Lilong Residences protected under the *Law of the People's Republic of China on Protection of Cultural Relics*, such as the national key protected cultural relic site Yuyangli and the municipal protected cultural relic sites Bugaoli and Shangxianfang. These sites are generally preserved and repaired in accordance with the aforementioned law and the rules for the implementation of that law. The focus lies in reinforcing severely aging brick-wood and brick-concrete structures while preserving the historical characteristics of their inner and outer profiles. In recent years, the materials, standards, and materials employed in such repairs have significantly improved. For instance, the characteristic unpainted brick walls of shikumen buildings have replaced earlier crude methods like exterior plastering, mortar joints, and brick cladding with more thoughtful ways such as brick restoration, polishing, and pointing using advanced techniques to prevent physical, chemical, and biological damage (see below).

Most of these cultural relic-status shikumen residences are public housing with limited relocation options for residents, leading to cramped living spaces with shared kitchens and bathrooms. It is difficult to fundamentally improve living quality and comfort. Historically, multiple families often had to share outdoor bathrooms, and current solutions include carving out tiny spaces within residences for sanitary facilities or dividing communal bathrooms into narrow units barely 60 cm wide for use by individual households. This results in a low-standard temporary transformation, which comes at the cost of diminishing historical spatial characteristics and quality. The pressing challenge is how to simultaneously address heritage conservation and residents' living conditions in these Shikumen Lilong Residences and whether a "temple within a snail shell" can indeed be created. This transcends a mere cultural and technical issue, evolving into a question of coordinated management in the context of socio-economic development. Given the limited applicability of legal, policy, and resource frameworks, current residents in Shikumen Lilong Residences find it difficult to relocate, and entrusting these residences to social management through national trusts is not feasible. The public participation model successfully employed in old urban area renewal in the West requires further experimental exploration within the realities of Chinese national conditions and property relations[24].

3.2 Tianzifang model

The Tianzifang model centers on revitalization through cultural creativity. Located on Taikang Road, Tianzifang covers approximately 2 ha. and consists of the east Lane 210 of "Tianzifang" (originally built in 1930 as "Zhichengfang"), the middle Lane 248 "Tianchengli", and the west Lane 274 "Pingyuanli". Due to the evolution from famous workshops in the Republic of China era to lane factories in the early times after the founding of the People's Republic of China, this area possessed spatial resources and historical significance as revitalization conditions for developing cultural and creative industries. At the end of the last century, the transformation and regeneration from Zhichengfang to an expanded Tianzifang began, with the core model emphasizing multi-party participation and shared interests. It started with government investment in infrastructure, followed by residents renting out their shikumen houses, and subsequently attracting artists, investors, and operators in and beyond China, thus forming a cultural and creative park of Shikumen Lilong Residences characterized by workshops for painting, photography, paper cutting, ceramic art, and glass art. This park creates spaces for cultural consumption like exhibitions, leisure, and cafés, energizing the lane and transforming Tianzifang into a globally recognized tourist attraction.

Tianzifang consists of narrow lanes that are only 3–4 m wide at most, with some less than 2 m wide, along with uneven block interfaces, forming a matrix of lanes. It is surrounded by various Shikumen buildings and other scenic spots, which have been shaped over the past 80 years. This diverse architectural landscape includes dominated modern shikumen structure, discernible old-style counterparts, stately western-style garden houses, dotted houses facing the lanes, modern residential buildings, and some abrupt fashion elements in recent years, creating a "collage" of the past and present, both recognizable and experiential. Particularly appealing to tourists, both domestic and international, are the intentionally retained weathered building exteriors that evoke a rustic Western aesthetic. It is precisely a place infused with Shanghai's historical memories and spatial experiences that lends a strong experimental character to the Tianzifang model through the activation of its cultural connotations and the release of its commercial energy. Indeed, this multi-faceted regeneration model preserves the matrix and substance of Shikumen Lilong Residences, revitalizing the entire neighborhood and embodying the dual meanings of economic and cultural rejuvenation. (Fig. 14)

Fig. 14 Aerial view of Zhang Yuan (or Zhang's Garden) featuring various lanes

However, this regeneration model faces practical challenges. With the increase in rental costs and imbalanced development of business activities, the sustainability of this regeneration and its potential for broader application have come under doubt. Nonetheless, one thing is certain: the Tianzifang model has pioneered the experimental model of cultural and creative spaces in Shikumen Lilong Residences. This model could potentially give rise to various adaptive variants that serve as a driving force for the revitalization and regeneration of urban historical environments. An ongoing similar revitalization case—Zhang Yuan—implements jacking and translation technology to relocate shikumen buildings to develop underground space, followed by returning them to their original positions. The aim is to provide spatial compensation for the overall protective renewal of Zhang Yuan. (Fig. 15)

Fig. 15   A scene at Tianzifang

3.3 Jianyeli model

The Jianyeli model focuses on renovation and anastylosis. Located within the historical feature area of Hengshan Road, Jianyeli was built in the 1930s and is one of Shanghai's typical Shikumen Lilong Residences, covering about 1.79 ha. It consists of 260 shikumen residential buildings classified as "excellent historical buildings" and is divided into three groups: east, middle, and west. This model serves as another experimental case for the regeneration of Shikumen Lilong Residences, following Tianzifang. The development entity comprises government and domestic and foreign developers, employing an approach of retaining and repairing the original west structures (40%) and carrying out demolition and anastylosis of the middle and east structures to incorporate high-end commercial transformations with hotel-style apartments (60%).[25] This combined intervention model of demolition, modification, and retaining has sparked widespread debate within the industry and beyond. Negative opinions dominate, questioning the feasibility of renovating or demolishing "excellent historical buildings" for anastylosis. The key considerations revolve around legality, the possibility of erasure, and the expertise required for design, construction, and management.

The Jianyeli model stands as a typical case worthy of reflection and offers insightful lessons, which can be summarized as follows:

First, while the Shikumen Lilong Residences serve as historical neighborhoods with a focus on residential use, the key conservation work includes the lilong matrix, scale, and overall appearance tied to urban memory. Even with the insufficient quality of buildings in the eastern and middle lanes, demolition and anastylosis need to consider their conservation categories and comply with corresponding application procedures, which is the premise of legal intervention.

Second, the partial demolition and anastylosis at Jianyeli can be viewed as a form of renovation.[26] (Note 8) The distinction here lies in that renovation merely needs to replicate the typical characteristics of the original structure and space, allowing for functional and creative improvements. In contrast, anastylosis demands a recreation closely resembling the original. Jianyeli failed to unlock the creativity of renovation, such as struggling to ensure harmonious and diverse coexistence and growth of old and new elements. It also failed to achieve the desired authenticity through anastylosis, such as neglecting to utilize original bricks and wood materials while focusing on detail reproduction. As a result, this led to skepticism and criticism.

Third, although it is undeniable that the "Jianyeli model" represents a unique approach to conservation and regeneration, the intervention methods should prioritize appearance preservation and internal renewal. Regulatory and creative renovations should follow these initial steps. Demolition and anastylosis are unsuitable for brick-wood mixed structures, as achieving the necessary height and precision for restoration is challenging. For many shikumen buildings that lack special conservation value, demolishing them and investing limited resources in unnecessary "restoration" is not worthwhile. (Fig. 16)

Fig. 16 Appearance of some reconstructed shikumen buildings in Jianyeli

3.4 Xintiandi model

The Xintiandi model focuses on transformation and renewal. The "Xintiandi" renovation project on Huangpi South Road derives its name from its proximity to the historic site of the 1st National Congress of the Communist Party of China (CPC). At the end of the 20th century, Benjamin Wood, an American architect, envisioned transforming the unprotected Shikumen Lilong Residences spanning 3 ha. into a vibrant hub for dining, shopping, and leisure consumption. This would be achieved through a "surgical" regeneration model and a business strategy focused solely on leasing rather than selling. Shikumen Lilong Residences, often referred to as the Shanghai equivalent of Hong Kong's Lan Kwai Fong, retained their original pattern and grain through meticulous repair and renovation of the old residential complex. Consequently, real estate developers received compensation in the form of development rights for 52 ha. of land in the Taipingqiao area.

The "Xintiandi" project has renovated most of the shikumen buildings on the site. The original unpainted brick walls were partially retained and reinforced, with surface repairs and some demolition and anastylosis (actually reconstruction) using old bricks and tiles. The project employed the brick wall repair technology of Germany-based Remmers Group to suit Shanghai's environmental climate, materials, and construction characteristics. Special reinforcing agents and water-blocking agents were used to manage common brick wall issues such as water seepage, wall loss, and moss growth.[27] (Note 9) The Jiangnan-style column-and-tie wooden roof truss was replaced by the original Western-style triangular roof truss, and the ground was paved with small black bricks rather than the original cement surface. The three-sided "Sanheyuan" courtyard in Shikumen Lilong Residences was transformed into indoor spaces, with the courtyard of each unit longitudinally connected to form a belt-shaped hall. These renovations, accented with Chinese-style decorative elements, have completely transformed the traditional Shikumen Lilong Residences into modern café spaces with Jiangnan charm. This represents a high-level creative design model for unprotected Shikumen Lilong Residences.[28] (Fig. 17 and Fig. 18)

Fig. 17 "Xintiandi" Shikumen Block Square   Fig. 18 "Xintiandi" Shikumen Longtang

Although the "Xintiandi model" has achieved great success in commercial development and cultural creativity, replicating this model has become challenging. The introduction of the *Property Law of the People's Republic of China* in 2007 sharply reduced compensation dividends, making the "Xintiandi model" unique. Nevertheless, in the preservation, revitalization, and regeneration of the unprotected Shikumen Lilong Residences, this model provides valuable insights and reference for future urban renewal projects.

4 Conclusions: Challenges and Countermeasures

Shanghai Shikumen Lilong Residences that are protected by cultural relics protection units or designated as excellent historical buildings include 260 protected neighborhoods and 350 protected land plots, which are primarily protected by laws and policies. The rest rely mainly on value judgment, policy regulation, and the balance between macro-control and market functions. When it comes to the conservation of Shikumen Lilong Residences, three key points cannot be ignored.

First, it is essential to prioritize type and quality over size and quantity. For large historical residences like Shikumen Lilong Residences, it is not necessarily better to preserve more. Instead, the focus should be on the completeness of type samples from each period and the improvement of preservation quality. For example, there are few preserved cases of old-style Shikumen Lilong Residences from the late Qing Dynasty and new-style Shikumen Lilong Residences from the 1910s-1930s as well as classic cases of "new style lilong" and "garden lilong" from the 1930s-1940s. Key samples should be conserved, researched, filed, and adapted for restoration, revitalization, and regeneration. Additionally, special research and filing are needed for repairs, additions, and reconstructions of Shikumen Lilong Residences since the founding of the People's Republic of China.

Second, conservation should be the premise, but revitalization and regeneration should be the goals to meet the evolving needs of life for architectural space function and quality. This approach ensures that Shikumen Lilong Residences remain vibrant and relevant for the present and future. It is necessary to rationally judge their value attributes, protect their identity, select and apply appropriate regeneration methods, and improve facilities for better research and practical applications.

Third, for many Shikumen Lilong Residences with average or poor quality, renovation is a vital method for reuse and regeneration. Although there is no standard answer to questions like which buildings to retain, reconstruct, or add, and how to integrate new and old materials and technologies, each regeneration project should be carefully considered. Each project must be individually discussed, comprehensively diagnosed, and tailored to its specific case to identify appropriate strategic options and solutions. This approach will address the goals and dynamics of sustainable economic and social development in the local area or region, providing a feasible path for the revitalization and regeneration of Shikumen Lilong Residences[26].

Notes

1. Although "markets stretching for miles" in Zhang Hu's *Travel Around Yangzhou* and the "thousands of lights brightening the night sky" in Wang Jian's *Night View of Yangzhou* both describe Yangzhou in the Tang Dynasty, it can be deduced that night markets were not exclusive to Yangzhou at least by the late Tang Dynasty.
2. The term "qiangmen" in *Basic Rules for Building* includes residence doors and doors on partition walls of inner courtyards. However, "qiangmen", also known as "kumen", specifically refers to res-

idence doors.

3. The *Land Regulation* has three versions: 1845, 1854, and 1869, which provide information about concession construction related to Shikumen Lilong Residences. The first version is more commonly referenced. See pages 46-49 in the *History of Shanghai International Settlement* by Kuai Shixun for details. This book is composed of two historical manuscripts from the *Shanghai Data Series: The System of Shanghai International Settlement* by Xu Gongsu and Qiu Jinzhang, and *History of Shanghai International Settlement* by Kuai Shixun, along with two translated versions.

4. The earliest version of *Land Regulation* refers to "thatched huts, bamboo houses, and wooden shacks". The word "liao" in the original Chinese text should be corrected to "liao" with the same pronunciation, but the former refers to bamboo ware or tea, while the latter denotes thatched huts, falling into the same category as bamboo houses and wooden shacks.

5. The *Venice Charter for the Conservation and Restoration of Monuments and Sites* (*Venice Charter*) has evolved over a long period. In 1926, the CICI was established in Paris, France. Its subordinate organization, the International Museum Office (IMO), hosted the First International Congress of Architects and Technician of Historic Monuments (ICATHM) in 1931 and released the famous *Athens Charter for the Restoration of Historic Monuments*. In 1946, the IMO's functions were replaced by the International Council of Museums (ICOM). In 1957, the First International Congress of Architects and Specialists of Historic Buildings was held in Paris, calling for independence from ICOM and joining the International Centre for the Study of the Preservation and Restoration of Cultural Property (ICCROM). In 1964, the Second International Congress of Architects and Specialists of Historic Buildings was held in Venice, approving the *Venice Charter* and establishing the International Council on Monuments and Sites (ICOMOS), which has since become a leading authority in the international discourse on built heritage.

6. Shanghai's built heritage includes 40 national key cultural relics protection units, 4,400 registered immovable cultural relics, 12 historical-feature areas (i.e., historical cultural districts) in the urban area (including 119 featured districts), 32 areas in the suburbs and Pudong New Area, 144 heritage conservation roads (including 64 roads under protection), 1,058 outstanding historical buildings, 13 national famous historical and cultural towns and villages, and 5 national "traditional villages" (see the relevant heritage protection list of Shanghai for details).

7. On the 60th anniversary of the founding of the People's Republic of China in 2009, the author was commissioned by the Architectural Society of China to write an article entitled "Shanghai Architecture and Its Urban Historical Context during Reconstruction", which discussed four protection models for Shikumen Lilong Residences. Over the past 12 years, both objective reality and subjective perception have changed greatly. This paper offers a second reflection on the four models, shifting the focus from conservation to regeneration.

8. Renovation is an intervention approach for the reuse and regeneration of buildings, playing a significant role in restoring vitality and improving the quality of old buildings that are seriously decayed. However, not all old buildings are suitable for renovation: they should have high heritage value and reasonable and legal protection identity. Before renovation, it is essential to determine which parts should be preserved and which should be renewed, as well as how new and old materials and technologies can be compatible (see Reference 26 for details).

9. After the technology of the Germany-based Remmers Group was successfully applied in the Xintiandi project, it was also used to restore the unpainted brick walls of the Building of China Merchants Steam Navigation Company. After 20 years of testing, the effect has proven to be good. See Chang, Q., Wang, F., & Wang, H. (2005). The revitalization of the century-old derelict building: Exterior restoration and interior renovation design of the Building of China Merchants Steam Navigation Company. *Architectural Journal, (5)*61; Qiu, X., & Zhang, M. (2008). Repair technology for historical buildings such as the Building of China Merchants Steam Navigation Company.

*Building Construction, (9)*43-46.; and Hu, Z. (Ed). (2008). *A story of Bund 9* (pp. 61-63). Shanghai Lexicographical Publishing House.

References

1. Yao, C. (1986). Supplemented by Zhang, Z. & reviewed by Liu, D. *Basic rules for building* (p. 41). China Architecture & Building Press.
2. Shen, H. (Ed.)./Shanghai Municipal Bureau of Housing Management. (1993). *Shanghai lilong folk houses* (p. 14). China Architecture & Building Press.
3. Kuai, S., et al. (Eds. or Trans.). (1980). *History of Shanghai International Settlement* (pp. 307-318). Shanghai People's Publishing House.
4. Kuai, S., et al. (Eds. or Trans.). (1980). *History of Shanghai International Settlement* (p. 49). Shanghai People's Publishing House.
5. Kuai, S., et al. (Eds. or Trans.). (1980). *History of Shanghai International Settlement* p. 54). Shanghai People's Publishing House.
6. Chen, C., & Zhang, M. (Eds.). (1988). *History of modern architecture in Shanghai* (pp. 160-164). Shanghai Joint Publishing.
7. Campbell, J. W. P. (2016). Traditional architecture in the United Kingdom (3), (pp. 58-61). *Architectural Heritage*. (Pan, Y., Trans.)
8. Zheng, S. (1999). *The evolution of Shanghai architecture in modern times* (pp. 146-151). Shanghai Education Publishing House.
9. Zheng, S. (2017). Reflections on architectural heritage conservation in Shanghai. Built Heritage, 1(1), 3-5.
10. Luo, X., & Wu, J. (Eds.). (1997). *Shanghai longtang* (pp. 2-4, 8-12). Shanghai People's Fine Arts Publishing House.
11. Wu, J. (1997). *A history of Shanghai architecture 1840-1949* (pp. 119-127). Tongji University Press.
12. Yang, B. (2003). *The combination history of Sino-West architectural culture in modern times of China* (pp. 233-241). Hubei Education Press.
13. Chang, Q. (2009). Shanghai architecture and its urban historical context during reconstruction. *Architectural Journal, (10)*, 24.
14. Chang, Q. (2003). *A conservative strategy of architectural heritage* (p. 4). China Architecture & Building Press.
15. Chang, Q. (2018). The past and the future: Critical cognition and practice of built heritage issues. *Architectural Journal, (4)*, 8.
16. Lowenthal, D. (1998). *The Heritage crusade and the spoils of history* (p. 6). Cambridge University Press.
17. Byard, P. S. (1998). *The architecture of additions* (pp. 77-79). W. W. Norton & Company.
18. Chang, Q. (2017). A Chinese approach to urban heritage conservation and inheritance: Focus on the contemporary changes of Shanghai's historic spaces. *Built Heritage, (3)*, 16-17.
19. Mason, R. (2016). On the theory and practice of value-centered historical protection. *Architectural Heritage, (3)*, 3-4. (Lu, Y., Pan, Y., & Chen, X. Trans.).
20. Machu Picchu Charter. (1979). *Urban Planning International, (00)* (Chen, Z. Trans.).
21. Chang, Q. (2019). Ancient and modern views of traditional architecture. *Architectural Journal, (12)*, 16.
22. Liu, G. (2016). Preservation and abolition of Shanghai Shikumen Lilong Residences. *Architectural Heritage, (4)*, 1-11.
23. Chang, Q. (2009). Shanghai architecture and its urban historical context during reconstruction.

Architectural Journal, (10), 23-28.
24. Li, B., Xu, X., Shao, Y., & Li, H. (2012). Research on public participation model in urban renewal. *Architectural Journal, (2)*, 134-137.
25. Lin, Y. (2016). A comprehensive review of Shanghai lilong conservation and renovation practice. *Architectural Heritage, (4)*, 12-20.
26. Broto, C. (2005). New concepts in renovation. Barcelona: Arian Mostaedi.
27. Dai, S. (2009). Protection and waterproofing of external facades of historical buildings. In Conservation and restoration technologies for cultural relics in China (Chapter Ⅲ, Section Ⅵ) (China Academy of Cultural Heritage, Ed.). Beijing: Science Press.
28. Luo, X. (2002). Research on architectural history, humanistic history, and the development model of Shanghai Xintiandi—old area renovation (pp. 74-75). (S. Y., Q, Z., Z, X., & L. W. Eds.). Southeast University Press.

Figures

Fig. 1 Shikumen Lilong Residences and urban grain of old Shanghai Source: Collected by the Shanghai History Museum (partial original figure)

Fig. 2 A source of early Shikumen Lilong Residences: Elevation of the gatehouse of Suzhou-style residence (qiangmen–kumen) Source: Plate 41 of Reference 1

Fig. 3 Typical Western-style storefront of late Shikumen Lilong Residences: Sidali, Lane 57, Shanyin Road Source: Third cover of *Architectural Heritage* (Volume 4, 2016) by Xi Wenlei

Fig. 4 Axonometric cross-sectional drawing of British brick-timber townhouses in the early 20th century Source: Page 61 of Reference 7

Fig. 5 Plan of early Shikumen Lilong Residence Hongdeli Source: Page 182 of Reference 6

Fig. 6 Profile of early Shikumen Lilong Residence Hongdeli Source: The same as Fig. 3-1

Fig. 7 Aerial view of late Shikumen Lilong Residence Bugaoli Source: Photographed by Zhu Donghai

Fig. 8 Plan of No. 172-196 at Bugaoli Source: Survey and mapping conducted by students from the College of Architecture and Urban Planning of Tongji University

Fig. 9 Ground floor plan of Bugaoli (double room and single room) Source: Drawn by Zhu Donghai

Fig. 10 Profile of No. 196 at Bugaoli Source: Survey and mapping conducted by students of the Department of Architecture of Tongji University during their internships

Fig. 11 Axonometric cross-sectional drawing of standard units in Bugaoli Source: Drawn by Zhu Donghai

Fig. 12 Exterior of 18th and 19th century workers' housing in Croix Rousse Source: Photographed by Chang Qing

Fig. 13 Aerial view of Xiafei Fang (Huaihai Fang) Source: Page 148 of *Inheritance: The Treasure of Heritage Architectures in Modern Shanghai*

Fig. 14 Aerial view of Zhang Yuan (or Zhang's Garden) featuring various lanes Source: Photographed by Liu Gang

Fig. 15 A scene at Tianzifang Source: Chang Qing Studio

Fig. 16 Appearance of some reconstructed shikumen buildings in Jianyeli Source: Chang Qing Studio

Fig. 17 "Xintiandi" Shikumen Block Square Source: Photographed by Wang Weiqiang

Fig. 18 "Xintiandi" Shikumen Longtang Source: Photographed by Wang Weiqiang

The Sustainable Urban Regeneration Models and Future of the People's Cities

Wang Lin
Professor at the School of Design, Head Professor at the China Institute for Urban Governance, and Director of the International Research Center for Innovation in Urban Regeneration and Preservation of Shanghai Jiao Tong University

This is an excerpt from the author's speech at the "2023 Global Cities Forum."

The Report of the 20th National Congress of the Communist Party of China(CPC) explicitly stated that China will "move faster to change the development models of super-large and megacities" and "carry out urban regeneration projects and improve urban infrastructure to build livable, resilient, and smart cities". The theory and practice of urban regeneration have evolved through stages from "urban reconstruction" to "urban revitalization" and finally to "urban regeneration" with the focus shifting from city to people, and the implementation path transitioning from "unified government management" to "collaborative governance". As urban development gradually shifts from incremental development to stock operation, Chinese cities have entered a new phase of "stock regeneration" and "high-quality development". Urban regeneration has become the new normal, and there is an urgent need for systematic review and innovative thinking regarding the relevant theories and methods.

Currently, Shanghai is actively exploring the establishment of a "sustainable urban regeneration model". The city has proposed that "urban regeneration should be regarded as a process of implementing the overall urban development plan, an important way to promote high-quality development, an essential carrier of modernization, and a crucial means to expand urban space, strengthen urban functions, upgrade urban quality, and enhance people's well-being, and it is necessary to deeply explore new approaches to urban regeneration under the new situation".

1 The Concept of People's City and the Development of Urban Regeneration

1.1 National strategy

"People's city is built by the people and for the people." This important concept was first articulated by President Xi Jinping during his inspection in Shanghai. He emphasized the need to manage the city meticulously like embroidery, to meet the higher demands of citizens for urban public spaces and living standards. The *Report of the 20th National Congress of the Communist Party of China* states, "To build a modern socialist country in all respects, we must, first and foremost, pursue high-quality development". The report further outlines the strategic decisions to "improve urban planning, construction, and governance, transform urban development models, and implement urban regeneration projects".

1.2 Current status and reflections on urban regeneration development

With the continuous implementation of supporting policies for urban regeneration from the central to local, various regions are actively exploring mechanisms for coordinated planning, sustainable models and supporting policies for urban regeneration. Additionally, by promoting local urban regeneration pilot projects, a range of replicable local urban regeneration practices have emerged. However, most cities are still in the preliminary stage of research and exploration, drawing on both domestic and international regeneration experiences while integrating their unique urban characteristics. The urban regeneration in the new development phase has undergone significant changes in concepts, goals, types, and mechanisms, forming a new situation with more diverse elements and richer layers, especially in regeneration types. Given the diversity of urban regeneration targets and the complexity of stakeholder interests in stock spaces, it is imperative to advance urban regeneration in a comprehensive, orderly, hierarchical, classified, regional, and systematic manner. This promotes the multi-dimensional adaption of regeneration governance scales, dynamic mechanisms, and regulatory elements, avoiding "one-size-fits-all" and "homogenization" phenomena due to unclear priorities or imprecise methodologies.

To avoid unsustainable urban regeneration that does not align with people's wishes and scientific principles, there is an urgent need to establish a national-level guiding framework, a local operable regeneration system, and an implementation supporting system. This will help address the specific challenges faced by different cities during their regeneration, clarify the priorities and refined implementation strategies for various types of regeneration work, streamline the relationships among diverse stakeholders such as governments, enterprises, and individuals, enhance the feasibility of regeneration planning and implementation schemes, and improve the precision and effectiveness of supporting policy systems, and innovate sustainable regeneration models tailored to local conditions.

1.3 Key regional regeneration strategies based on international experience and Shanghai practices

1.3.1 Organic regeneration strategies for Central city

Firstly, there is the strategy of "overall planning and regional regeneration", which entails adhering to advanced planning and design concepts, fully considering the future urban needs, and ensuring orderly, unified, and coordinated regional development. Secondly, there is the strategy of "environment first and overall balance", which prioritizes the improvement of the regional landscape and environmental quality to drive the overall renovation and upgrading of the area. By applying the concept of plot ratio transfer in planning, the overall balance should be achieved through overall planning, thereby avoiding the unchecked building height and density in central urban areas due to the blind pursuit of high plot ratios. Lastly, there is the strategy of "organic regeneration with the preservation of historical features." This strategy adopts an organic regeneration model that preserves and revitalizes historic architectural clusters, preserving historical features while meeting the needs of modern life. It fully integrates the preservation of historical features with organic regeneration.

1.3.2 The Features Blocks Protection and Regeneration Strategy

Firstly, the organic combination of protection and regeneration, preservation and new construction should be upheld. 1)It is essential to take the path of integrating preservation and regeneration by assessing the values of the historical features to determine which parts to preserve or demolish, avoiding blanket preservation, ensuring harmony between old and new buildings and land use functions to foster the city's organic growth. 2) Innovative breakthroughs in the existing technical regulations should be made. In historical features, the architectural scale, layout, and texture of lanes and alleys significantly differ from current technical regulations. To preserve the original space pattern, the block elevation, it is necessary to propose technical planning regulations appliable to the historical features blocks. For new construction projects within the blocks, targeted and detailed protection and reconstruction plans can be employed to ensure the specific implementation. Furthermore, specific land planning policies should be formulated for historical features blocks as designated regenerated areas. Firstly, a clear policy on plot ratio incentives should be established. Within the heritage preservation blocks, construction following the principles of "historical features preservation, maintenance, and inheritance" should be incentivized with a policy disregarding plot ratio restriction. Such buildings exempted from plot ratio restriction can be used for both public or non-public functions that align with urban functions and regional needs. The on-site (or nearby) plot ratio transfer should be encouraged to advance the implementation of land planning policies. Importantly, it can foster holistic sustainable development and multi-faceted win-win scenarios for urban culture, society, and the economy. Secondly, it should be clarified that heritage conservation neighborhoods , as designated areas for urban regeneration, are not bound by conventional technical standards. Instead, a "site-specific policy approach" should be adopted, with urban design and detailed planning serving as the legal basis.

1.3.3 Strategies for the transformation and regeneration of industrial areas

First, enhance overall industrial transformation by advocating the concentrated transformation of stock industrial land areas, encouraging functional platform collaboration with sub-district and town, organizing dispersed land rights holders for overall transformation. Second, it is crucial to strengthen the preservation of industrial heritage. During the process of industrial transformation, efforts should be made to preserve industrial civilization. Strengthen the protection of industrial heritage by inheriting industrial civilization during transformation, ensuring industrial heritage protection and utilization, combining protection and organic regeneration. This requires systematic research and assessment, overall planning and collaboration, and a heritage-based approach to regeneration and development. Third, establish specific industrial regeneration zones to form three differentiated "one plot, one policy", including "collaborative transformation, autonomous transformation, and government expropriation and reservation". Fourth, enhance support for industrial land transformation by adhering to the principle of "use first", innovating systems and mechanisms, and giving localities more space and vitality to revitalize stock.(Fig. 1 and Fig. 2).

Fig. 1 Boston South Bay

Fig. 2 Wusong Industrial Park

1.3.4 Micro-regeneration Strategy for Street Public Spaces

First, it is essential to clarify the design approach to the micro-regeneration of street public spaces. This necessitates adopting a systematic mindset and progressive guidance to establish design rules from macro, meso, and micro levels, including street guidelines and architectural street facade guidelines (Fig. 3). It requires holistic thinking and a problem-oriented approach, involving a comprehensive examination of issues across various facets of street spaces to identify all problems and challenges and develop a task list. Additionally, meticulous thinking and a detailed breakdown of elements are required. This involves the breakdown of street components, followed by both holistic and localized studies of the current state of each category and item. Second, the implementation path for the micro-regeneration of street public spaces should be formulated with a blend of professional, governance, and smart thinking.

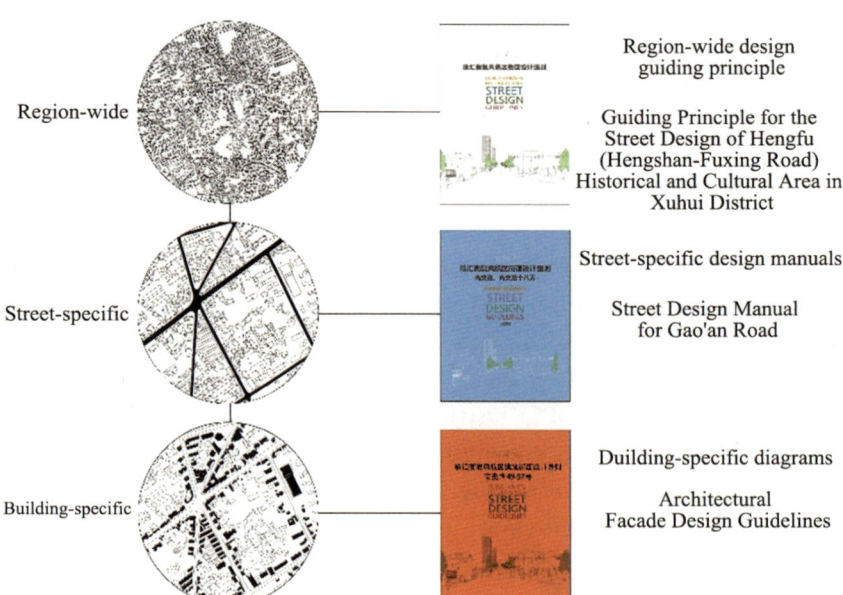

Fig. 3 Progressive Design Schematic

The implementation path should rely on professional forces, combining rigid control and flexible guidance, adhering to multi-party governance, social participation, process management, and using intelligent management and long-term control to enhance governance efficiency.

1.4 Reflections on the Construction of an Urban Regeneration Classification System and Classification Principles

Urban regeneration is a systematic endeavor that involves not only the renovation of existing physical spaces but also the intricate and diverse socioeconomic relationships underlying these spaces. Currently, there exist diverse studies on urban regeneration classification from perspectives such as the roles, subjects, and patterns of regeneration and renovation intensities. However, a systematic and refined framework has yet to be formed to guide local practices in the classification of urban regeneration. Therefore, we propose a people-centered principle, which stipulates that urban regeneration classification in the new era should embody the principles of regeneration for the people, by the people, and with its outcomes shared by the people, and the concept that "people's city is built by the people and for the people" should be consistently integrated into the classification process of urban regeneration, with people's needs, participation, and consensus serving as the key considerations in defining regeneration categories.

Through research into several key areas in Shanghai's urban regeneration, this study aims to construct a scientific classification system for urban regeneration through analysis, which emphasizes key aspects and promotes collaborative implementation. This system framework and construction principles, along with several countermeasures, are proposed to better guide local urban regeneration actions towards standardization, systematization, and sustainability.

2 Urban Regeneration Classification Models and Practical Exploration

2.1 Classification system of urban regeneration in Shanghai

From the *14th Five-Year Plan to Vision 2035*, and from the promulgation of *Shanghai Urban Regeneration Regulations* to the introduction of the *Shanghai Urban Regeneration Action Plan*, Shanghai has explicitly outlined its urban regeneration objectives: comprehensive regional regeneration, human settlement quality enhancement, public space facility optimization, historical charm revitalization, industrial park transformation and innovation, and commercial and office district renovation and upgrading.

According to *Shanghai Urban Regeneration Regulations* and the *Shanghai Urban Regeneration Action Plan*, six key areas in Shanghai's urban regeneration have been identified: historical feature conservation and regeneration, residential area regeneration, public space regeneration, industrial park transformation and regeneration, commercial and office district regeneration, and comprehensive regional regeneration. To deepen the understanding of regeneration content, study regeneration models, and guide regeneration actions, Shanghai's urban regeneration is categorized into six major categories, twenty-nine intermediate categories, and ninety-two sub-categories (Fig. 4).

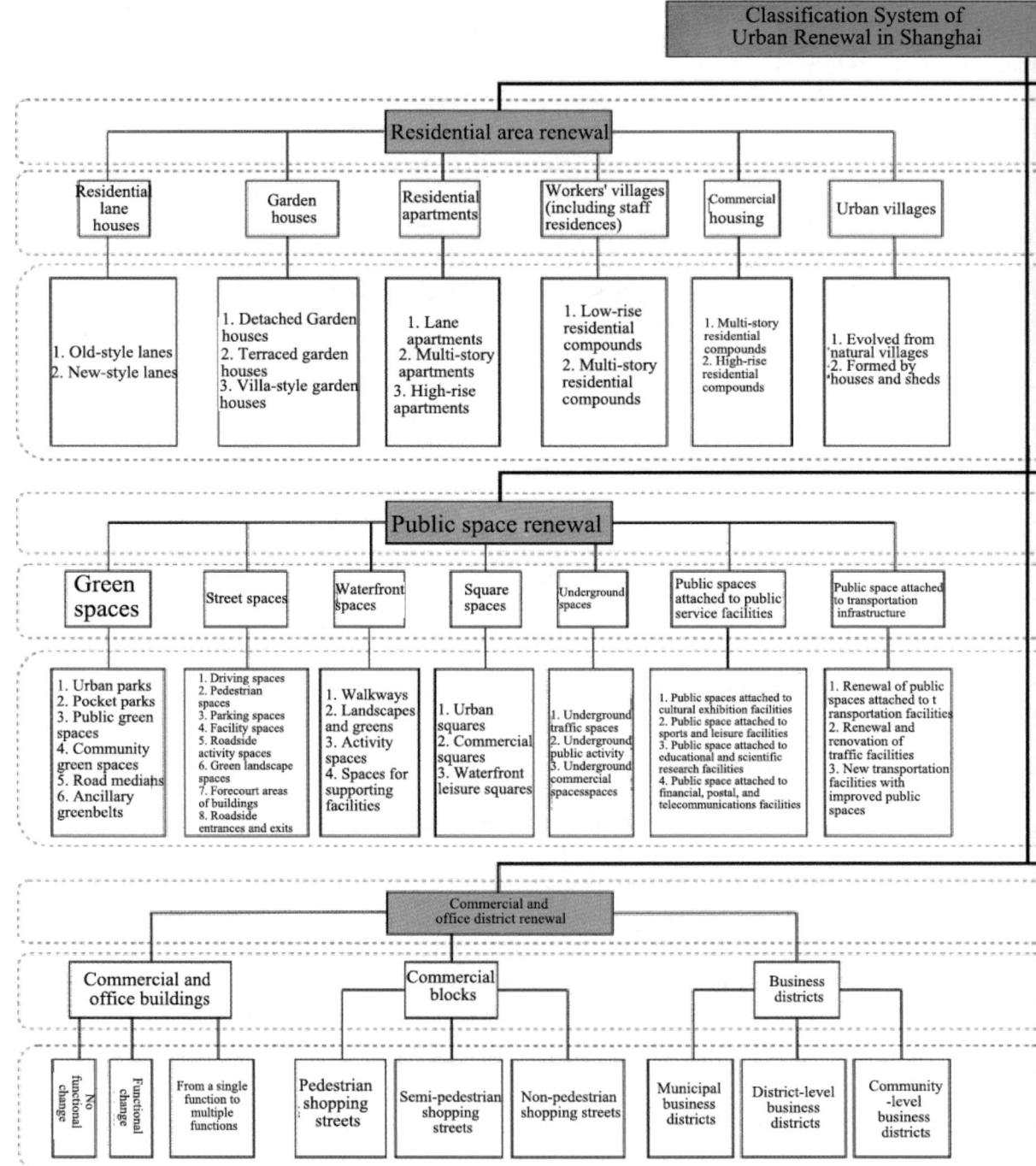

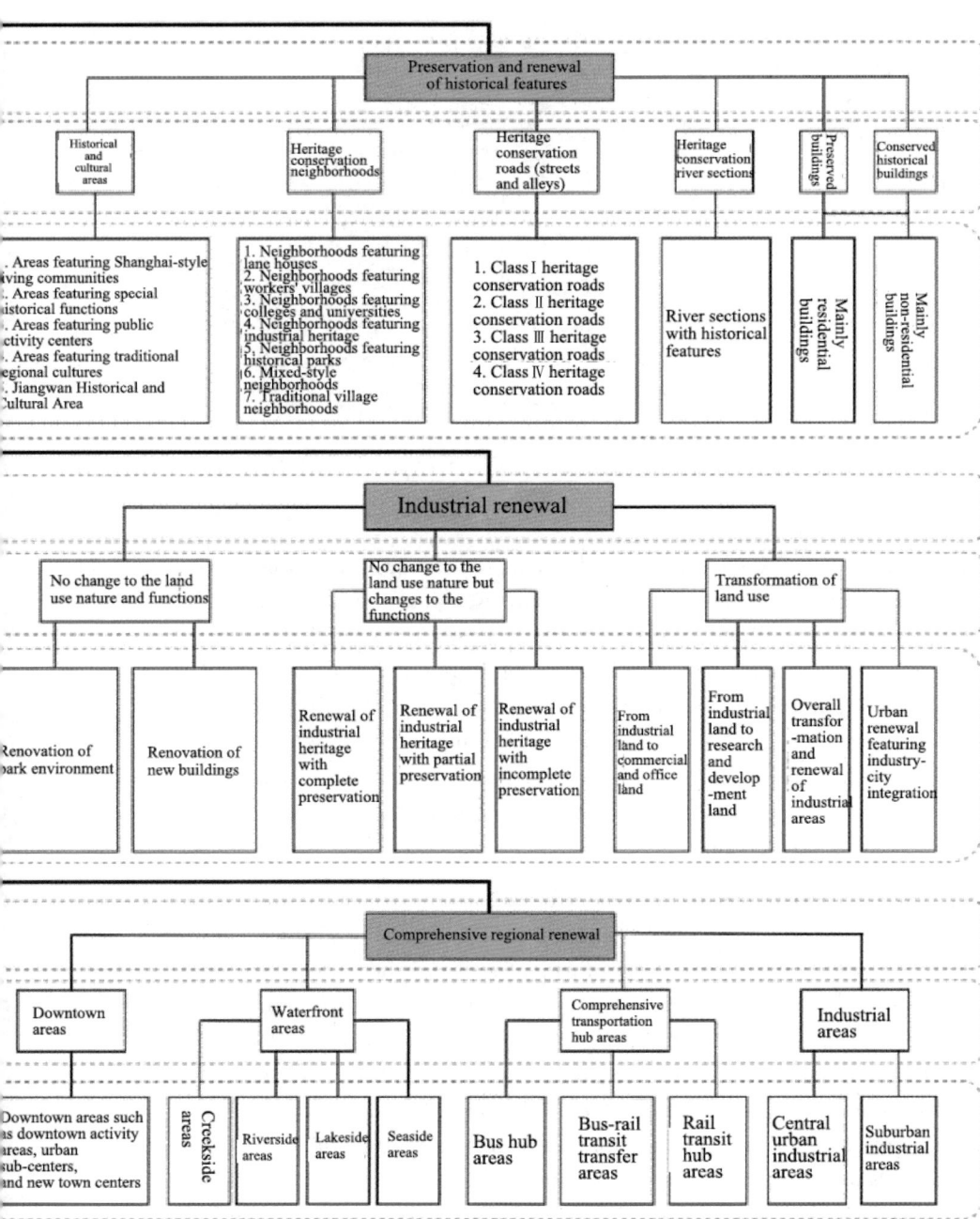

Fig. 4 Classification System of Urban Regeneration in Shanghai

Chapter V Urban Renewal and Digital Empowerment

2.2 Types and practices of urban public space regeneration

Urban public spaces encompass plazas, streets, waterfront areas, ancillary spaces for public facilities, the exterior spaces of buildings, and green spaces (Fig. 5).

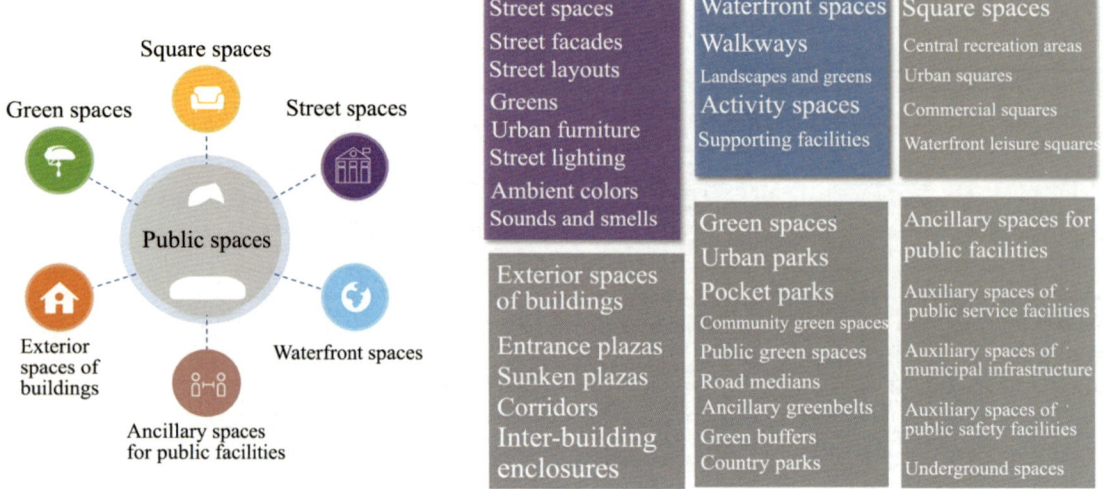

Fig. 5   Types of Urban Public Space Regeneration

2.2.1 Micro-regeneration of urban street public spaces

There exist numerous issues with the current state of urban streets: first, inadequacies in comprehensive and detailed landscape design elements; second, deficiencies in urban street design schemes which exhibit excessive control but insufficient guidance for adaptive updates; third, the lack of collaboration among multiple departments involved in street design formulation, management, and implementation; fourth, inefficient implementation mechanisms for urban street design, leading to a lack of long-term sustainability. Addressing the relationships between the whole and the parts, between coordination and diversity, and between rigid control and flexible guidance, is a crucial task in refined street governance.

Regarding the design strategies for the micro-regeneration of urban streets, the first key point is to take a refined approach to street urban design. First, we should utilize systematic thinking and progressive guidance: Region-wide, street-specific, and building-specific guidelines should be established respectively. This includes formulating a region-wide design guiding principle, street-specific design manuals, and building-specific diagrams for building facade design. Second, we should embrace holistic thinking and a problem-oriented approach: A blanket, multi-faceted, and all-around assessment should be conducted. This involves comprehensively examining and identifying issues across various facets of street spaces, examining the preservation of the historical features of streets, clarifying a list of problems and key challenges, and formulating a task list for subsequent governance work. Third, we should employ meticulous thinking and element refinement: A categorized, all-encompassing, and more meticulous design approach should be adopted. Street elements should be subdivided, and a comprehensive and localized study should be conducted for each category and item. This allows for the determination of control and guidance directions on a case-by-case basis, ultimately leading to the formulation of overall control principles and detailed control rules for each category and item.

The second key point regarding the design strategies for the micro-regeneration of urban streets is to take a systematic approach to refined street governance. First, a professional mindset is required, which involves leveraging specialized expertise and combining rigid control with flexible guidance. Second, a governance-oriented mindset is required, which involves multi-party collaboration, social participation, process management, and adherence to the mechanism of "unified planning, unified implementation, collaborative management, and joint governance". Third, a smart mindset is required, which emphasizes intelligent management, long-term dynamic control, and enhanced governance efficiency.

For instance, the west entrance of Shanghai Library, through negotiation between the library and the government, yielded 1.5 m of green space to the pedestrian walkway, achieving community co-governance. The refined urban design of the landmark Wukang Building widened the pedestrian walkway by 3.6 m, satisfying the touring needs of visitors and making the Wukang Building a popular tourist attraction in Shanghai (Fig. 6).

Fig. 6　Refined Urban Design of the Landmark Wukang Building

Chapter V　Urban Renewal and Digital Empowerment

In summary, the innovative thinking behind the micro-regeneration of urban streets is that the streets of the people should be built by the people and for the people, emphasizing a "people-oriented" approach rather than a "car-oriented" one. It advocates "unified designs" rather than "uniform designs" and emphasizes "guiding the public" instead of "constant rectification".

2.2.2 Micro-regeneration of urban waterfront spaces

The micro-regeneration of urban waterfront spaces aims to create urban public spaces that are characterized by high-quality regeneration, refined management, and premium vitality. We have established a comprehensive evaluation system for public spaces, which encompasses multiple domains such as spaces, landscapes, communities, culture, hinterland expansion, and social governance. Through a thorough investigation and assessment of the current state of the urban core sections along the Huangpu River and Suzhou Creek in Shanghai, we have proposed strategies to enhance the quality of the public spaces along the Huangpu River and Suzhou Creek.

We systematically established a facility system for waterfront public spaces, conducted a thorough survey of the current status of facility management and maintenance, visited various districts to draw experience, and constructed an all-encompassing facility system for the Huangpu River and Suzhou Creek. We proposed governance strategies for all-encompassing, refined, and comprehensive management of facilities, as well as policy formulation and institutional guarantees. The strategies encompass various aspects such as management objects, content, and methods, financial support, and legal regulations (Fig. 7 and Fig. 8).

Fig. 7 Original Wusong Road Gate Bridge Pier Renovated into "Waterfront Urban Terrace"

Fig. 8 Urban Regeneration of the Suzhou Creek Waterfront Space on the North Bund, Hongkou

3 Reflections on the Future Trends of Urban Regeneration

In the new era of development, urban regeneration models have undergone tremendous and profound changes in terms of regeneration concepts, connotations, objectives, methods, tasks, and mechanisms. The evolution of urban regeneration research content reflects a transition from a sole focus on physical spaces to applied policies and eventually toward comprehensive mechanisms. Regeneration concepts now emphasize wholeness, systematic approaches, and sustainability, while regeneration mechanisms underscore joint participation from government, the market, and society.

Urban regeneration should involve meticulous urban design to create human-centered urban spaces; enhance the characters of neighborhoods to promote artistic and cultural consumption; and activate urban vitality to shape shared spaces for the public. By employing innovative thinking, high-quality regeneration, refined management, and premium vitality, implementing a sustainable urban regeneration model becomes achievable, aligning with the concept of a people-centric city.

Cultural Metaverse Empowers Urban Cultural Innovation

Xie Xuefang
Secretary of the CPC Committee of the School of Humanities, Tongji University; Distinguished Professor of Changjiang Scholars Program, Ministry of Education; Special Committee for Cultural Metaverse, China Cultural Industry Association

This is an excerpt from the author's speech at the Forum on Inheriting Historical Context & Building Sci-Tech New City.

Although the concept of the "metaverse" was proposed as early as 1992 by Neal Stephenson in "Snow Crash", it wasn't until 2021 that the metaverse became a popular term in various fields in China. The metaverse is a fusion of new-generation information technologies such as AI, blockchain, 5G, IoT, and VR. Transitioning from the metaverse to the cultural metaverse signifies the process of the metaverse empowering the cultural domain. For the development of a city, the cultural metaverse will play a crucial role in the entire innovative development process of urban culture.

1 Connotation Interpretation of Cultural Metaverse in the Era of Digital Intelligence

What is the metaverse? Although the concept of the metaverse originates from the West, in the context of Chinese modernization, it focuses on how to leverage the metaverse to empower the digital economy and tell the Chinese story of the cultural metaverse. Simply put, the cultural metaverse can be defined as the three-dimensional synergy and unification of technology, content, and scenarios. First is the technological dimension, where the essence of the metaverse lies in technological innovation, including AI, blockchain, VR technology, and digital twin technology. The metaverse acts as an aggregator, integrating these technologies and clustering them within the space built with the metaverse scenario. Second is the content dimension, where content innovation is the true core of metaverse space. The core support of the metaverse scenario is creative content, and the cultural metaverse is the space where the metaverse empowers the development of urban culture, with culture being its primary element. Third is the scenario dimension, where the cultural metaverse represents and presents itself through scenarios, which are key to making the metaverse visible, usable, and accessible.

2 Cultural Metaverse Empowers Urban Cultural Innovation

The global metaverse industry is increasing its investment in resources and policy support, as a new wave of technological revolution and industrial transformation is deeply evolving into urban spaces. Based on the "system" of urban culture that we constructed in our earlier research, which, for the development of a city, consists of urban cultural life, urban cultural production, and urban cultural ecology, forming the entire "system" of urban culture.[1] We now transplant this into the theoretical construction dimension of the cultural metaverse empowering urban cultural space. In the era of the cultural metaverse, urban culture is embracing digitization, intelligence, and experiential enrichment. Blending with the metaverse's characteristics, the urban cultural space in the era of digital intelligence will be a new urban cultural landscape composed of digital cultural life, digital cultural production, and digital cultural ecology.

First, understanding urban cultural spaces from the theoretical connotation of the cultural metaverse involves distinguishing between cultural digitization and the cultural metaverse. We can explain this using three keywords or concepts of three spaces. The first is a virtual cultural space. What is the difference between VR, AR, and AI cultural projects and the metaverse? The fundamental difference lies in the first attribute: the cultural metaverse creates a virtual cultural space that immerses users in a lifelike experience, achieving a true integration of virtual and real elements. Second, it is a digitized cultural space, achieving the transformation into a digital form. In the 1.0 era, we considered going online and networking, but in the 2.0 era, we think about digitization. The metaverse itself is actually about blending immersive experiences with the connection between the virtual and the real elements of the digital twin. The last is a networked cultural space. Starting in the 1990s, with the United States as a representative, we entered a stage of development marked by the rise of a network society. The metaverse, as an extension of internet technology, represents the application and presentation of Web 3.0. By distinguishing between these three spaces, we can clearly understand the relationship between metaverse technological innovation and urban cultural spaces. In fact, technology serves to better provide a visual and digital representation across the entire industry chain, from creativity and production to operation. In conclusion, the metaverse era emphasizes creating an immersive experience for urban culture, with urban culture being its essence and root. Each city has its unique cultural DNA and a distinct cultural spirit core. In an era of rapid technological advancement, our goal is to better present these cores and develop various models for presenting urban culture.

Second, urban cultural spaces have become the interaction between the physical cultural space and the virtual cultural space. In recent years, there has been a growing number of cases combining urban cultural spaces with the metaverse. Quanzhou in

---

1 Huang Changyong, Xie Xuefang. Construction and Practice of China's Urban Culture Indicator System. Academic Monthly, 2017. 49 (05): 102-115.

Fujian Province has integrated intangible cultural heritage with the metaverse, Xi'an has created metaverse scenarios and developed VR projects, and Beijing has presented VR projects at the Forbidden City. These examples have shifted urban cultural spaces toward digitization, experience orientation, and intelligence, breathing new life into traditional Chinese culture and catering to the cultural preferences of Gen Z and post-95s. For the future development of urban culture, the metaverse brings about two spaces of a future city: the current physical space and the digitization and cultural innovation within it, and the vast digitized virtual cultural space that is infinitely expandable. For instance, many foreign luxury brands are not only designing clothing and accessories for real humans in the physical space but also for digital humans in the virtual space of the metaverse. It can be said that both virtual and physical cultural spaces are two sides of the same coin in the overall innovation of urban culture. Certainly, the cultural metaverse is not just the presentation of so-called virtual cultural space but the interaction and fusion of the virtual and the real.

Third, the metaverse has become a new way to tell compelling urban cultural stories. In recent years, several provinces and cities in China have utilized the creation of metaverse scenarios to narrate local cultural stories, with various AR exhibitions and VR light shows being manifestations of the metaverse. Particularly, the "Red Culture Metaverse" has gained traction, with many regions starting to use local revolutionary cultural resources to build their own "Red Culture Metaverse". For example, Shanghai's "Digital 1st National Congress of the CPC", Jinggangshan, and Red Flag Canal are leveraging metaverse scenarios to innovate the expression of revolutionary culture. In fact, the main difference between the metaverse space and traditional physical space exhibitions is that it allows the audience to immerse themselves in that period of revolutionary culture and history. This immersive experience enables Gen Z or post-95s to better experience, understand, and appreciate that revolutionary history and culture, achieving a deep-seated impact that resonates in their minds and hearts. This in turn becomes a new way and means to effectively convey revolutionary culture.

Fourth, digital collectibles within the metaverse space have become an innovative expression of urban culture. In recent years, digital collectibles have been dedicated to creatively integrating Chinese traditional culture. For example, Chinese-style architecture in the metaverse space serves as the 2.0 version of digital collectibles and also represents an architectural space within the metaverse. However, this architectural space is a virtual one, akin to an architectural space in the metaverse world with Eastern aesthetics. When combined with the sale of digital collectibles, it becomes a new format and model for digital collectibles, as well as a new way to expand urban cultural spaces.

3 Metaverse Empowers New Entity of Urban Culture

In September 2022, the Ministry of Industry and Information Technology of the People's Republic of China, in collaboration with four other ministries, released the *Three-Year Action Plan for Innovation and Development of the Metaverse Industry (2023-*

2025). The plan outlines measures to build advanced metaverse technologies and industrial systems, providing policy-level guidance to empower urban innovation and development through the metaverse. With this policy boost, regions across China are actively creating new metaverse scenarios around the cultural tourism metaverse, cultural museum metaverse, and performing arts metaverse, essentially creating a second space of cities to achieve synergy between virtual digital space and real physical space. For instance, Zhangjiajie Planet uses XR integrated interactive technology to create an immersive experience metaverse platform featuring a myriad of fantastic peaks, making it stand out and come alive on the city's map.

The metaverse empowers urban cultural development, introducing a new entity, known as digital humans. Each of us can have our own digital avatar, allowing us to participate in metaverse space scenarios through these avatars. In fact, digital humans have become a standard feature of metaverse spaces, such as professional virtual staff in museums, virtual artifact workers, virtual tour guides in cultural tourism institutions, virtual teachers in the digital education field, virtual anchors, virtual actors in the media industry, and more. In other words, in the future, digital humans will exist in every field, extending to every corner of the city's cultural space and serving as a vital entity in the continuous expansion of urban spaces. For example, in Xi'an Museum's digital art exhibition, visitors can enjoy 61 exhibits by taking a 10-minute tour through their digital avatars. In addition, in recent years, local Spring Festival galas have introduced new formats such as using AI technology to "resurrect" deceased celebrities for joint performances and remote showcases. This is an integration of core metaverse technologies such as AI technology, VR technology, and digital twin technology. Particularly with the rise of AIGC (Artificial Intelligence Generated Content) technology, the construction and content presentation of metaverse scenarios have been made more cost-effective and efficient, showcasing the greatest difference of the metaverse—any progress in blockchain technology, AI technology, or VR technology will propel the metaverse forward in leaps and bounds. For instance, Shanghai has implemented several metaverse scenarios including "Horizon of Khufu"and "Luoyang", which serve as typical examples of this trend.

4 Balance Between Technology and Culture

The metaverse itself is an integration of technologies, actively embracing each new technology to better empower the development of urban cultural spaces. For the development of each city, it is essential to manage the relationship between technology and systems effectively. With the deep development of AI large model technology, the authenticity of photos, audio, and video content generated by AIGC has become indistinguishable, giving rise to a new term "deep-fake". This means that in the future, several contents generated by AIGC may be applied to metaverse spaces, potentially leading to new security issues and copyright problems. This implies that behind the cultural development of each city, there should be inheritance and protection at the institutional level. Particularly concerning the application of such new technologies in the two spaces of urban culture, cultural security issues must be considered to achieve a balance between technology and culture.

Throughout the history of technological development and cultural development, there have been highly overlapping and similar patterns of evolution. For urban cultural innovation, new technologies bring forth the presentation of different cultural DNA for each city, meaning that every region possesses its unique cultural context and genes. We utilize technology to better awaken the cultural DNA of a city, rather than to destroy it. This is done to strengthen and preserve, forming what is known as the gene of urban digital culture. Therefore, on one hand, in the era of digitization and intelligence, for empowering urban cultural development through the metaverse, it is essential to adhere to concepts of sharing, co-creation, co-construction, and co-governance. On the other hand, it is important to strike a balance between the "blank spaces" and the "preservation of the old" in the process of urban cultural development. Why do we protect and inherit architecture and intangible cultural heritage? It is to preserve the "old". In the virtual urban cultural space, achieving creativity + symbiosis is necessary for the "blank spaces", which means that "blank spaces" and "preservation of the old" should foster a symbiotic and prosperous coexistence of the old and new cultures, rather than a form of replacement or destruction. Furthermore, regardless of how the metaverse and AIGC technology develop and iterate, the ultimate goal is to better serve the sustainable and innovative development of the entire urban culture, enabling every individual in the city to enjoy a better cultural life. Putting people at the core has always been the intrinsic benchmark in handling the relationship between technology and culture in urban cultural development.

The Practice of City Information Modeling for Urban Governance

Yang Tao
Associate Professor, School of Architecture, Tsinghua University

This is an excerpt from the author's speech at the City of Digitalization, Brightness of Intelligence Forum.

In the 21st century, globalization, localization, digitalization and characterization are mixed together to create more heterogenous scenarios for urbanism, and as a result the city tends to become a product composed of various scales of physical entities and virtual spaces, sustaining real-time dynamic communications between different groups of activities and events. In 2017, the concept of digital twin city was proposed in Xiong'an New Area designated as a national pilot city for the next generation of urbanism in China, aiming to explore a new mechanism of promoting eco-oriented development in China. The Comprehensive Planning of Xiong'an New Area sought to establish a synchronized planning and an orchestrated construction of both the digital and the real cities , and this can be interpreted as the primary idea of a digital twin city in China.

In this context, the idea of the city information modeling (CIM) platform had been suggested to support the construction of the digital twin city of Xiong'an New Area, in order to promote the modernization of urban governance system and to advance its capacities. According to the guideline of the CIM platform issued by the Ministry of Housing and Urban-Rural Development (MoHURD) in China, the CIM platform is defined as a complex of urban information flows and transactions embedded in the three-dimensional digital spaces, in which the above-ground and the underground, the indoor and the outdoor, the current and the future spatio-temporal data are recorded and integrated by deploying a package of the tools of Building Information Models (BIM), Geographic Information Systems (GIS), Internet of Things (IoT) and other ICTs. As a result this will sustain and optimize the full life-cycle processes of urban planning, design, construction, governance and management. The CIM platform offers basic functions, such as data mining and analysis visualization, professional model simulation and management assessment, as well as various intelligent services for urban construction and operation.

In order to establish the digital twin cities in China, the idea of city information modeling (CIM) has been widely discussed and several pilot cases have been announced by the MoHURD since 2018. They are Xiong'an New Area; New Subcentre of Beijing, Guangzhou, Xiamen and Nanjing. In 2020, the MoHURD together with other ministries released the concept of a new type of city infrastructure in which the CIM is treated as the basic platform supporting intelligent civil infrastructure, smart city and intelligent network of vehicles, urban security and resilience, intelligent construction and building industrialization, urban comprehensive management as well as smart communities. More pilot cases therefore have been assigned by the MoHURD. After this, the State Council announced the guidance for a new business and a new model for a new consumption in which the CIM is also considered as one of the new tools for facilitating a new economic development, focusing on urban digitalization. When the concept of the CIM was incorporated into the 14th 5-year development planning in China, it demonstrated that the CIM, as the operating system for a digital twin city, has become one of the key powerhouses in enhancing a new round of green urbanism proposed by the Chinese government, which aimed to achieve carbon neutrality in the near future.

The CIM proposed in China has its own vision, which can be divided into three parts. The first is to offer a new way of spatial sharing for citizens, departments and industries. All the spaces could be shared by all the stakeholders in the full life-cycle of planning, construction and governance. For instance, in Xiong'an pilot project, each space with sematic address, generated by knowledge graph, has an ID. For such a space, all the information, either population or economic transactions, could be marked to be related to that space. All the events and activities taking place within that space could be restored and could be sent out for others to use.

The second is to change the way of spatial governance focusing on the bottom-up processes. The CIM can be deployed to observe fine-scaled items or individual activities taking place in rooms and streets. For example, the malfunction of fire alarmer, the services of community clinics and/or the sales promotion on streets, can be detected in the real time and then being simultaneously sent out to the people who can take care of those issues. As a result, the localized information can be aggregated to help governments and stakeholders to respond to and tackle with the more globalized problems in a more accurate way. This could sustain and advance the people-centred governance in China.

The third is to explore a new method of increasing the transition of spatial values. The urbanization in China in the past 30 years has been driven by land economy, because all the cities could get new plots of land for development each year. But now the Chinese government has proposed the strategies of green development and carbon neutrality. Thus, for most of the cities, they no longer have large pieces of new land. The cities have to develop, redevelop, or regenerate within the existing development boundaries. The digitalized spaces however offer new locations of transaction and communication, and meanwhile, those digital data have an opportunity to move around beyond the physical boundaries of the cities. Thus, those digital data can be transformed into new digital assets and even digital capitals via the tool of the CIM with respect to more globalized networks. Essentially, the CIM will become a new powerhouse of urbanism facilitating digital economies.

As far as the development of Xiong'an New Area is concerned, the construction of digital twin city is one of its key objectives. This includes three aspects. The first is the construction of digital intelligent infrastructure, aiming to support the digitalization of future development of the whole city. The second is the establishment of pervasive intelligent environment. By which, public spaces or indoor spaces in the physical city are full of ubiquitous intelligent sensors and services, sustaining various convenient interfaces between residents and machines/built environment. The third is to realize the concepts of digital asset transaction, digital asset management and digital economy innovation. This seeks to serve as a new driving force of urbanization in the inner land of China, and embraces the birth of new urban forms. In the context, this section focuses on how the CIM is constructed, and how the CIM can be used for the administrative processes of urban planning, architectural design, construction and governance, as well as for revealing the relationship between the CIM and urban governance.

The CIM platform of Xiong'an has one key task and four breakthroughs. The key task is to create synergy between the digital and the real cities. The basic and interactive element is *the space perceived, felt and experimented by the people who live and work in Xiong'an*. This space can be occupied by people reflecting on how Xiong'an grows, trying to find regularities in planning, design and construction, embodying how it is developed, finding digital patterns recorded in the digital world, and showing how people digitally interact with each other.

The prototype of the CIM platform started from the existing, and comprehensive planning, regulatory planning, design and construction to completion. When a building information model was completed, it would be disassembled into water systems, electronic systems and others regarding different disciplines, and each system would be integrated with a system of IoTs or sensors. Then, they would be reorganized into a new and intelligent existing system that could be evaluated to explore how Xiong'an works or operates. This would then optimize the efficiency of urban governance.

Around the key task of spatial synergy, this CIM platform also has four breakthroughs. The first keyword is *time*. As discussed above, the platform records six stages of the existing, planning, design, construction, operation and completion of Xiong'an New Area. In this way, the digitalization of Xiong'an can be realized along the temporal processes of urban administration and governance.

The second is *algorithm*. It aims to integrate data that might be collected from building information models, geographical information systems, various sensors, socio-economic census, as well as all documents generated from the administrative processes. All those data are elaborately mined by using different algorithms, and the connections among data are automatically marked with space and/or time.

The third is *space*. All elements are located within certain spaces. However, within each discipline and industry, such as building construction or traffic management, each space has different rules. In the real world, these varying rules help us physically construct a building or operate a traffic system. Within the digital world, all these rules need to be connected together in order to intelligently support various scenarios of urban construction and operation. For instance, if we evacuated people from a fire in the building, we should have informed the people inside the buildings, while simultaneously contacting hospitals to arrange ambulances, arranging firefighters to be at right places and rooms at right time, and even advising traffic control to block entries to the building. Thus, all the information should be sent out to every relevant department and/or individuals according to the spaces where they should be located, and meanwhile this process is driven by the space-based rules set up by human beings. When these social rules are embedded into the digital world, it would help us solve problems in the city or optimize urban governance.

The fourth is *sharing*. The above example of fire evacuation is also an example of sharing. The sharing of knowledge on the evacuation actually means the creation of a collaborative way of evacuating people. All the procedures could be transparent for the relevant stakeholders, and meanwhile all the necessary elements could be collaboratively provided by the different stakeholders or markets. This offers a new way of creating new mechanism of operating and evaluating buildings, blocks, communities and cities.

Xiong'an project of the CIM includes three deliveries, namely *the digital platform, the innovative policies and the data standards*. The digital platform, seeking to gather all the data from the six stages of the existing and operation, comprehensive planning, regularity planning, design, construction, and completion, at the very least provides a data board of a digital city for Xiong'an. All the data have been reorganized and assigned to digital spaces. All the elements/items can be calculated by various kinds of software. Based on this, the platform firstly aims to exhibit how Xiong'an New Area looks, and visualizes how the city could be managed by citizens and stakeholders. Then, the platform offers search tools to explore all the information calculated and simulated within the platform itself, and also provides an interactive tool to assist users and decision-makers to operate the real city. In the end, the platform, based on the blockchain technologies, will advance the application of transacting data, in order to explore more innovative ways of surfing in the digital world.

However, this digital platform needs to be supported by the innovative policies on the creative modifications on the procedures of planning, construction and management across the administrative departments. By which, all the information generated by the platform can easily flows through the departments and the related industries. For example, architects are not fully engaged in the construction process in China, but the innovative policies in Xiong'an set up new rules for architects to be fully engaged in the construction process and even in the operation of the buildings via the digital platform. The innovative modifications of planning permission process and fabrications offer opportunities for construction enterprises to be engaged in the lifecycle of the management processes ranging from planning to operation.

The digital platform, together with innovative policies, cannot work without data standards. For the project of Xiong'an, the data standards formulated across 17 industries and 14 disciplines have covered the full life-cycle of urban construction and operation, and have been elaborately set up according to the scenarios of urban governance and the methods of digital modeling.

The logic of urban construction and operation has been incorporated into the CIM of Xiong'an. For urban construction, all the rules have been digitally assigned to the stages from planning and design to construction. On the whole city level, the development goals, such as innovation, resilience, happiness, livability, greenness and so on, have been set up to correspond to each spatial unit, perhaps in the form of the regulatory planning unit. However, the CIM firstly explores mapping these goals to various specialized units, such as functional units, green infrastructure units, morphological units, energy units, or ecological units, and all of which, equipped with different rules, have different sizes. Then, all kinds of performance objectives are digitally disassembled on the different units and implemented on each plot, and this therefore constitutes geometric and data analysis, corresponding to morphological and index assessment. Finally, these indicators or rules are assigned and then implemented on the levels of buildings and facility components. In this way, the targeted development goals can be decomposed at the sequential stages, ranging from planning to design, construction and completion assessment.

For urban operation, this logic is reversed. From building components to plots, to various specialized units, and finally to Xiong'an as a whole, the living data of urban operations are gathered and calculated layer by layer, which is used to evaluate whether the overall goals of cities are achieved. Therefore, this constitutes a closed loop of planning, construction, monitoring and adjustment.

This new logic of planning and construction is driven and facilitated by various models including basic mathematics, statistics, geography analysis, big data mining, and intelligent algorithms. At the same time, the CIM not only includes professional models, such as regional economic model, population model, traffic evaluation model and so on, it also comprises of more comprehensive urban models like urban growth boundary model. Of course, the CIM platform can't ignore the role of expert team, and offers the tools of creating deep interaction between machine and expert team in time. By which, all the models have been optimized by and iterated with the professionals and the stakeholders.

When processing those models, the threshold values for each space and each period are designed to judge whether the planning and design goals are achieved at the right places and at right times. If the threshold is broken, the CIM can automatically make a comparison between different variables to evaluate. For example, whether public service facilities and population match, whether the actual population increment exceeds the allocation of public service facilities, and/or whether the service performance ability needs to be improved. During the evaluation process, the new adjustment schemes would be proposed and compared with each other. It is not only the comparison of advantages and disadvantages of the schemes, but also the impact assessment. For example, for a certain plot, when the energy supply of a plot increases, will urban heat island effect around the plot be altered? In the process of optimization, different decision-making modes are set up, including tactical adjustment, facility adjustment and planning adjustment. For example, in the transportation field, the change of red and green signal lights is a tactical one, the change of parking lot is facility adjustment, and the modification of comprehensive transportation planning system is planning adjustment. In this sense, this builds a closed loop of early warning, evaluation, scheme comparison and optimization.

All the analyses, even our deduction and judgment of the future, depends on data. As we move into th future, it is particularly important for the internet of things to perceive the real- time data. Through the seamless coverage of the internet of things, natural environment, social environment, behavior patterns and other data would be effectively collected, so as to draw a picture of the future of the city through data management. This is *a new way of digitally monitoring of urban development performance*.

In addition, there exists an index standard of design and construction, such as floor area ratio and line sticking rate, which can be regarded as *the inherent construction gene of the city as an entity*. Then, is there a correlation between *the "entity" construction gene* and *the "virtual" operation performance*? Machine learning can help us reveal the underlying factors. For example, a science park with good performance - e.g. street vitality, patents per capita, and energy consumption - depends on the support of land mixing degree, greening level, road network accessibility, housing rent index, or coffee shop density. After establishing the association between operational performance and construction genes, it can be applied to open public regulations on design and construction, so that it can help ordinary people participate in urban construction or urban operation management more conveniently and rationally, and then establishing a good communication and interaction channel among citizens, experts and the government.

In general, the CIM of Xiong'an is essentially based on the establishment of a digital information system with full life-cycle, full time and space, full elements and whole process, the core of which is to optimize the allocation of spatio-temporal resources, especially to re- examine the allocation of spatial resources from the temporal dimension, and to establish a planning and governance model of real-time collaborative feedback.

On the basis of the CIM, the digital twin city can be established so that people can be immersed in the digital world more easily andalso navigate between the digital and the physical worlds in a smoother manner. It then generates the ecology of the digital twin cities. This will promote digital transformation in the near future. Some creative industries, such as digital filming, media, advertisement and digital finance, will be optimized by using the digital twin. This is based on data capital centers that establish well-defined data assets, and this could be finalized by digitalized urban governance. This will be supported by data nodes and data bound in the future. All these things will be supported by the digital government, as well as the cutting-edge research on technology. We think that basic research is of the uttermost importance, and the innovation of various industries is also the key to helping us generate an ecology of the digital world.

In conclusion we argue that a digital twin city is not merely the virtual replica of the real city, but it is evolving based on the big data or real time data. Its capacity strengthens, with the evolution of digital technology, to become an infinite realm with human physical environment, social activities and collective minds. Digital twin cities will evolve into the synaesthetic city and develop the soul of the physical city. Digital technology empowers the physical reality, by which human perception and cognition of cities can be enhanced like never before. Digitized cities and citizens will create new methods of sensing. The future city revolution will be trigged across the world and the evolution of cities will be accelerated.

Planning Strategies and Tactics for Urban Renewal in Beijing

Shi Xiaodong
Chief Planner of Beijing Municipal Commission of Planning and Natural Resources and Director of Beijing Municipal Institute of City Planning & Design

This is an excerpt from the author's speech at the "2023 Global Cities Forum".

President Xi Jinping points out that the correct use of strategies and tactics has been key to the CPC's glorious history, monumental achievements, and continuous victories in the face of various risks and challenges. As China's urbanization enters its later stages, the importance of understanding planning strategies and tactics for urban renewal cannot be overstated.

In my decades of planning experience, I've also reflected on the nature of urban planning. While some question its scientific basis, I view planning as a public policy that maps social, economic, political, and cultural factors onto physical space. The vitality of this public policy depends on the extent to which it impacts people's right to survival and quality of life. High-quality spaces create positive impacts, while poorly planned areas lead to inefficiencies. Urban renewal, as a type of urban planning, is a systematic expression of policy. It's not about demolishing an old world to build a new one, but rather about renovating and upgrading the existing world. This process connects economic and spatial factors, rights and responsibilities, and public and individual interests. Meanwhile, urban renewal is also comprehensive, involving issues such as planning and design, preservation of historically significant cities, ecological restoration, and even safety concerns. It must serve to improve the current living environment, foster economic development, and enhance commercial vitality, while also meeting future needs. Many cities in China aim to position themselves as world-class, global centers. However, they also face numerous historical issues that need to be addressed through urban renewal efforts.

To effectively carry out urban renewal and address various challenges spanning the past, present, and future, a "three-in-one" support system is needed: clear objectives, scientific development, and strong organization. Only with clear objectives can diverse interests be unified. Relevant policies in Beijing and Shanghai are continuously being improved, with numerous policy mechanisms and action plans being introduced. These policies clarify project determination mechanisms, policy support content, and overall coordination capabilities, facilitating the implementation of action plans and initiatives. Implementing the action plan for urban renewal is an effective means of achieving high-quality development. Scientific development must embrace the important concept of a "people's city", using urban renewal to promote the city's spirit and character, enhance its capacity, create a high-quality living environment, inherit historical heritage, improve urban competitiveness, and strengthen the city's soft power. Urban renewal also requires corresponding social organizations with capabilities whether in economic, institutional, or public awareness. These include design capabilities, policy capabilities, operational capabilities, and financial support capabilities.

Since the 18th CPC National Congress, Beijing has undergone three historic transformations. As the political center, Beijing hosts numerous state institutions. The first transformation is shifting from being a super-large city to focusing on the development of the capital itself, ensuring the development of its functions as the nation's capital. The second transformation is moving from a single city to coordinated development with urban agglomerations and metropolitan areas. The third transformation is transitioning from management to significant governance. By alleviating non-essential functions and optimizing resource allocation in the peripheral areas, Beijing seeks high-quality development methods to address the urban maladies of an ultra-large city.

In this context, there are two main threads. First, Beijing emphasizes the functions of the "Four Centers". The overall positioning of Beijing is as the national political center, cultural center, science and technology innovation center, and international communication center. All city functions, including management services and public services, need to be developed to strengthen the functions of these "Four Centers", requiring functional updates. The second main thread is promoting social renewal oriented by improving people's livelihoods, enhancing the environment, driving economic development, and boosting consumption. This requires the participation of all social groups and involves the renovation of residential spaces, production spaces, and public spaces.

In this context, Beijing has clarified its approach to urban renewal. Beijing's urban renewal is based on existing assets, using neighborhoods as units, with existing buildings as the main focus, and guided by the improvement of functional environments. It adopts a small-scale, gradual, and minimally profitable yet sustainable approach, aiming to improve functionality, enhance quality and efficiency, and improve people's livelihoods, while strictly controlling large-scale demolition and reconstruction.

From the perspective of the overall planning framework, urban renewal requires the establishment of a system with clear objectives and directions. Therefore, Beijing's urban renewal efforts have constructed a five-dimensional system of "Space-Method-Organization-Motivation-Implementation". This system uses space as a carrier, focusing on the different functions, positions, characteristics, and requirements of urban spaces, highlighting differentiation. Over years of practice, a methodology has been developed that establishes a working method distinct from the previous large-scale demolition and construction. The organization system consists of diverse governance, Party building guidance, and grassroots participation, with a core in joint organization and leveraging the collective strength of districts, counties, sub-districts, townships, towns, banks, and enterprises. The motivation system, acting as the engine driving the renewal process, comprises numerous systems, standards, and policies. Lastly, the implementation system aims to establish long-term mechanisms to ensure sustainable renewal outcomes.

In the spatial system, urban renewal emphasizes a people-centered approach, which is consistent with both Beijing and Shanghai. Beijing's total urban construction area amounts to 1.7 billion square meters, of which existing structures account for 1 billion square meters. The primary focus of urban renewal is on the renovation and enhancement of these existing structures, while also incorporating new developments. This is a daunting task.

In the methodological framework, Beijing's urban renewal emphasizes coordinated neighborhood planning. The city has delineated over 1,300 neighborhoods, with 178 of them designated for renewal. Six main categories of central neighborhoods have been identified, each with customized technical approaches and policy tools. The methods are refined through practical implementation. From the block renewal process in Beijing's Huilongguan and Tiantongyuan areas, a comprehensive and iterative renewal approach has been developed, creating a "Four-Step, Eight-List" working model. The first step is identifying problems through urban health assessment and evaluation based on territorial spatial planning, forming a list of problems and resources; the second step is multi-stakeholder consultations to determine needs, summarizing resident demands such as "no traffic jams while driving, no overcrowding on the subway, no flooding on rainy days, no waiting for services, nearby employment opportunities, places to play chess and chat, places to run and walk, and places to park", creating lists of needs and visions; the third step entails overall planning and policy alignment, resulting in strategy and policy lists; the fourth step is creating action plans and implementation measures, resulting in task and project lists. Considering the characteristics of existing areas, six major implementation strategies and 36 implementation points are proposed, including public service enhancement, transportation improvement, infrastructure support, quality enhancement, optimization of work-life balance, and refined governance and co-governance.

In the organizational system, it is essential to strengthen diverse co-governance. First, we should adhere to government guidance by using major projects, such as investments in public spaces and rail transit construction, as opportunities to leverage diverse participation. Second, we should strengthen market entities and encourage market-based approaches to mobilize existing assets. Third, we must encourage resident participation to truly understand their "urgent needs, difficulties, worries, and expectations". For example, Wangjing Walk was originally a side street filled with parked vehicles. Through renewal efforts, the government transformed this side street into a pedestrian commercial area. By utilizing urban public resources and attracting private capital, it has become a small but popular spot that people like to visit and share on social media.

In the driving force system, innovative policy mechanisms are crucial. Beijing has formed a "1+N+X" urban renewal policy system. In this system, "1" refers to the top-level design documents at the city level, including urban renewal regulations, special plans, guiding opinions, and action plans. "N" represents categorized guidance policies, including those targeting various renewal objects such as single-story houses (courtyards) in core areas, old residential communities, old factories, old buildings, inefficient industrial parks, public spaces, and infrastructure. "X" refers to targeted "small-scale" policy documents and standards addressing bottleneck issues in the renewal process. This includes the formulation of urban renewal incentive policies in areas such as planning, land use, finance, taxation, construction, operation, management, and approval processes. The focus is on clearing bottlenecks in urban renewal.

In the implementation system, it is necessary to define the rights and interests of the implementing entities and ensure their benefits. In addition to state-owned assets, when identifying these entities, we must also pay close attention to centrally-owned assets, military-owned assets, and other types of ownership. Determining the rights and interests of the entities is the basis of the entire renewal operation. Sometimes these rights and interests are clear, and sometimes they are not. The *Regulations of Beijing Municipality on Urban Renewal* propose a public safety baseline. In cases where property rights are highly complex, the district government needs to assume the corresponding entity rights and interests.

Secondly, it is important to ensure that participating entities benefit not only from social, cultural, and environmental gains but also from economic returns. It should be clearly established that property management companies can form new entities through cooperation with other market players, creating new scenarios through partnerships or shareholding, and granting corresponding rights to participating social entities. In this process, some policy breakthroughs are inevitable. For instance, the five-year transition period policy states that for renewal projects developing new industries and business models supported by the state and the city, if they comply with planning and do not change the main land user, relevant industry authorities can provide certification documents allowing these projects to enjoy a transitional policy of land use according to the original purpose and rights type. Upon expiration of the 5-year transition period or when transfer requires land use procedures, these can be processed through agreements according to the new purpose and new rights type. The land use rights renewal policy extends the land use duration and determines land prices comprehensively. It allows for a "rent first, transfer later" approach to land use, with rent payable in annual installments, thus reducing initial investment costs for businesses. The mixed-use land policy provides clear support for coordinating all types of land use functions, ensuring compatibility between different land plot usage types, legally and compliantly converting the purpose of existing buildings and others.

Moreover, urban renewal processes are often constrained by regulatory requirements such as fire safety and landscaping. These constraints can be alleviated by optimizing and fine-tuning the planning approval process. For instance, in fire safety design, performance-based renovations that are no less effective than the current situation can be adopted to address cases where new fire safety regulations cannot be fully met during the renewal process.

All of the above are some of Beijing's considerations and measures in system design and policy during the previous phase. In summary, urban renewal is a challenging task with a long road ahead, requiring sustained effort and long-term commitment. I hope to have more opportunities to learn from Shanghai's valuable experiences in urban renewal. Your critiques and corrections are welcome. Thank you!

Appendix: Theme Activities and Series Activities of World Cities Day 2023

S/N	Time	Events	Theme	Venue	Organizer(s)	Type
1	June 7	The second session of the United Nations Habitat Assembly: World Cities Day Side Event & World Cities Day Themed Exhibition	Towards a multilateral collaboration and knowledge exchange system to accelerate SDGs implementation in cities	Headquarters of UN-Habitat (United Nations Human Settlements Programme) in Nairobi, Kenya	Ministry of Housing and Urban-Rural Development, Shanghai Municipal People's Government, and UN-Habitat	Series activity (overseas)
2	April 11	"World Cities Day into Campuses" at Shanghai University of International Business and Economics	Jointly Promoting Sustainable Urban Development	Siyuan Lecture Hall, Library of Shanghai University of International Business and Economics, No. 1900 Wenxiang Road, Songjiang District, Shanghai	Shanghai Coordination Center of World Cities Day and School of Languages of Shanghai University of International Business and Economics	Series activity
3	May 26	"World Cities Day into Campus" at Shandong University	Showcasing the Charm of Diversified Cities and Jointly Promoting Green Sustainable Development	Yifu Information Building of Shandong University (Central Campus) / Online Tencent Meeting	Student Career Guiding Center of Shandong University, School of Foreign Languages and Literature of Shandong University, and Shanghai Coordination Center of World Cities Day	Series activity
4	June 16	"World Cities Day into Campus" Theme Seminar for Teachers and Students of Fudan University & Outreach Course on Urban Anthropology	—	Floor 9, Jiujiang Building, No. 137, Jiujiang Road, Huangpu District, Shanghai	Shanghai Coordination Center of World Cities Day and Institute of Anthropology and Ethnology of School of Social Development and Public Policy of Fudan University	Series activity
5	June 22	"World Cities Day · Wanli" Neighbourhood Life Festival Opening Ceremony and Fifteen-Minute Community Life Circle Orienteering Competition	Paradise in City, Full of Vitality	From Shanghai Jinhua Private Middle School to the Sports Center	Shanghai Coordination Center of World Cities Day, Sports Bureau of Putuo District, and Wanli Subdistrict Office of Putuo District	Series activity
6	July 11	"Sustainable and Resilient Urban Tourism" — "Urban Events · Business Discussion" Cultural Tourism Salon	Sustainable and Resilient Urban Tourism	Floor 1, Brand Pavilion (Pedra Alta), Shipyard 1862, Pudong New Area, Shanghai	Shanghai Modern International Exhibition Co., Ltd. of Donghao Lansheng Expo Group	Series activity

(continue)

S/N	Time	Events	Theme	Venue	Organizer(s)	Type
7	August 6	"Vernacular Architecture Inheritance Camp - Shexian County Stop" Series Activities	Inheriting Craftsmanship and Protecting Culture	Jintan Village, Kengkou Township, Shexian County, Huangshan City, Anhui Province	Management Committee of Vernacular Architecture Protection and Development Special Fund of China Foundation for Cultural Heritage Conservation	Series activity
8	October 20	"Yangtze River Delta · Orderly Development and Utilization of Geothermal Resources" Forum	Yangtze River Delta · Orderly Development and Utilization of Geothermal Resources	Shanghai Science Hall	Geological Society of Shanghai, Geothermics Committee of Chinese Geophysical Society, Geological Society of Jiangsu Province, Geological Society of Zhejiang Province, and Geological Society of Anhui Province	Series activity
9	October 25	CALLS FORUM 2023—Dialogue on Fine Urban Management of Suzhou Creek and Seine River	Fine Improvement and Empowerment of Soft Waterfront, Block, and Community Environment for Urban Renewal and Industrial Revival	The Bund Historical Memorial Hall, Huangpu District, Shanghai	Office of the Leading Group for Strengthening Fine Urban Management in Huangpu District, Regional Work Office of Huangpu District, Waitan Sub-district Office of Huangpu District	Observance
10	October 25	2023 Shikumen Urban Renewal Forum and Launch Conference for the Compilation of *Classic Examples Album of Shikumen* Urban Renewal	—	Jinchao Lane 8	Shanghai Institute for Global City, Shanghai Coordination Center of World Cities Day, Shanghai Dianshan Lake Forum Development Promotion Center, and Committee on Population, Resources and Environment of Shanghai Committee of China National Democratic Construction Association	Series activity
11	October 28	Awarding Ceremony of the Global Award for Sustainable Development in Cities (Shanghai Award) and the Opening Ceremony of 2023 World Cities Day China Observance	Financing Sustainable Future For All	The Grand Halls	Ministry of Housing and Urban-Rural Development, Shanghai Municipal People's Government, and UN-Habitat	Observance
12	October 29	Inheriting Historical Context & Building Sci-Tech New City Forum	Inheriting Historical Context & Building Sci-Tech New City	Jiu Ke Shu (Shanghai) Future Arts Center	Shanghai Municipal Commission of Housing and Urban-Rural Development, the Science and Technology Commission of Shanghai Municipality, Shanghai Municipal Administration of Culture and Tourism, and the Fengxian District People's Government of Shanghai	Observance

(continue)

S/N	Time	Events	Theme	Venue	Organizer(s)	Type
13	October 29	2023 Global Cities Forum	Financing Sustainable Future for All	Dalinghao Bay Conference Center	The Development Research Center of the Shanghai Municipal People's Government, Shanghai Municipal Commission of Housing and Urban-Rural Development, Shanghai Jiao Tong University, UN-Habitat, the World Bank, and the Minhang District People's Government of Shanghai	Observance
14	October 29	2023 World Cities Day "Urban Environment" Theme forum and the 4th Shanghai International Urban Furniture Summit Forum	Improving Urban Environment Quality, Building a City with Ecological Resilience	Donghua University	Shanghai Municipal Commission of Housing and Urban-Rural Development, Shanghai Leading Group Office for Promoting Fine Urban Management, Shanghai Municipal Bureau of Ecology and Environment, China Association For Standardization, and Donghua University	Observance
15	October 30	Global Urban Forum on Social Governance Innovation and Sustainable Development	—	Shanghai Convention & Exhibition Center of International Sourcing	Tongji University, Shanghai Municipal Commission of Housing and Urban-Rural Development, and the Putuo District People's Government of Shanghai	Observance
16	October 30	Green Development and Financing for Sustainable Development Forum	Green Development and Financing for Sustainable Development	Shanghai International Convention Center	Shanghai Municipal Commission of Housing and Urban-Rural Development and Shanghai Media Group	Observance
17	October 29	2023 "Shanghai-Tokyo" Sino-Japanese Urban Delicacy Management Symposium	Craftsmanship Attains Quality Renewal	Jiu Ke Shu (Shanghai) Future Arts Center	Shanghai Municipal Commission of Housing and Urban-Rural Development and Shanghai Fengxian Government	Observance
18	October 29	Mayors Forum on High-Quality Urban Development and 40th Anniversary of Mayors' Training	—	The Grand Halls	Department of Building Energy Efficiency and Technology, National Academy for Mayors of China (Professional Training Institute of Housing and Urban-Rural Development), and China Association of Mayors	Observance
19	October 29	Forum of Sustainable Transportation and Future of Cities	Intelligence Low Carbon Resilience Sharing	Museum of Art Pudong	China Highway & Transportation Society and CAST UN Consultative Committee on Transport & Sustainable Infrastructure	Observance

Appendix

(continue)

S/N	Time	Events	Theme	Venue	Organizer(s)	Type
20	October 29	Urban Environmental Security Resilience and Humanistic Care Construction and Development Forum	—	Shanghai Branch of China Academy of Urban Planning & Design	China Academy of Urban Planning & Design and FII CHINA	Observance
21	October 30	2023 International Cities and Construction Industry Forum	Urban Future & Industrial Opportunity	Broadway	China Council for the Promotion of International Trade Construction Industry Branch and Shanghai Municipal Commission of Housing and Urban-Rural Development	Observance
22	October 29	Forum on Urban Environmental Management and Water Environment Sustainability	—	Shanghai World Expo Center	Technology and Industrialization Development Center of the Ministry of Housing and Urban-Rural Development, Management Committee of China-Singapore Tianjin Eco-city, China Construction Technology Consulting Co., Ltd., and Public Utilities Board of Singapore	Observance
23	October 29	International Forum on Green and Low-carbon Building Technologies	Collaborate for Green Development, Co-create a Low-carbon Future	Shanghai World Expo Center	Department of Standards and Norms of the Ministry of Housing and Urban-Rural Development and National Center of Technology Innovation for Green and Low-Carbon Building	Observance
24	October 29	Chinese Urban High-Quality Development Forum	Sustainable Housing and Communities	Shanghai World Expo Center	China Construction News	Observance
25	October 29	City of Digitalization, Brightness of Intelligence Forum	—	Shanghai World Expo Center	Information Center of the Ministry of Housing and Urban-Rural Development, Asia Pacific Office of United Nations Human Settlements Programme (UN-Habitat), and Shanghai Municipal Commission of Housing and Urban-Rural Development	Observance
26	October 30	Forum on Science and Technology Empowering the Construction of Better Houses and Supporting the Sustainable Development of Cities	Science and Technology Empower the Construction of Better Houses and Support the Sustainable Development of Cities	Shanghai World Expo Center	Technology and Industrialization Development Center of the Ministry of Housing and Urban-Rural Development	Observance

(continue)

S/N	Time	Events	Theme	Venue	Organizer(s)	Type
27	October 30	2023 Housing Rental Symposium: Sharing the Sustainable Future - A Road for High-Quality Rental Development	Sharing the Sustainable Future - A Road for High-Quality Rental Development	Shanghai World Expo Center	China Institute of Real Estate Appraisers and Agents and Zhejiang University of Technology	Observance
28	October 30	2023 Shanghai-Espoo Sustainable Development Thematic Event	Promote the Inter-city Cooperation in Sustainable Development through UN Agenda 2023	Shanghai Academy of Social Sciences	Institute of Urban and Demographic Studies of Shanghai Academy of Social Sciences and Foreign Affairs Office of Espoo	Observance
29	October 28	The Third SDG Cities Global Conference: SDG Cities Hub and Practice Seminar	SDG Cities Hub and Practice	Tongji University	UN-Habitat and Tongji University	Observance
30	October 29	The Third SDG Cities Global Conference: Technical Workshop: SDG Cities Deep Dive	SDG Cities Deep Dive	Tongji University	UN-Habitat and Tongji University	Observance
31	October 29	The Third SDG Cities Global Conference: Expert Seminar: The Exploration and Development of UMF-Shanghai Adapted Index	—	Tongji University	UN-Habitat, Tongji University, and Shanghai Coordination Center of World Cities Day	Observance
32	October 29	The Third SDG Cities Global Conference: International Corporation on Urban SDGs in the Post-Covid Society	International Corporation on Urban SDGs in the Post-Covid Society	Tongji University	International Research Center of Big Data for Sustainable Development Goals, CAST UN Consultative Committee on Comprehensive Research of Work Disaster Risks, UN-Habitat, and Tongji University	Observance
33	October 29	The Third SDG Cities Global Conference: Urban Finance Seminar – Towards A Local Finance Framework	Towards A Local Finance Framework	Tongji University	UN-Habitat and Tongji University	Observance
34	October 30 - November 1	Shanghai International City and Architecture Expo 2023	Green and Low-carbon Cities, Smart Transformation and Development	Shanghai World Expo Exhibition & Convention Center	UN-Habitat and Shanghai Municipal Commission of Housing and Urban-Rural Development	Observance

Appendix

(continue)

S/N	Time	Events	Theme	Venue	Organizer(s)	Type
35	October 31	Global Observance of World Cities Day 2023	Finacing Sustainable Urban Future for All	Üsküdar in Istanbul, TÜrkiye	UN-Habitat, Municipality of Üsküdar in Istanbul, Türkiye	Observance
36	November 22	2023 "World Cities Day" Community Financial Literacy Forum in Shanghai, China	Gathering Financial and Economic Strengths to Create a Better Community	Xuhui University of Continuing Education Shanghai	Xuhui University of Continuing Education Shanghai (Xuhui Institute of Community Education Shanghai) and Partnership Office of Network Hesse-China	Series activity
37	November 30	Integration of Healthcare and Elderly Care, Fusion of Medical and Preventive Services - 2023 "World Cities Day" Elderly Rehabilitation Collaboration and Exchange Conference in Shanghai, China	Integration of Healthcare and Elderly Care, Fusion of Medical and Preventive Services	Xuhui Riverside Party-Mass Service Center	Xietu Community Health Service Center in Xuhui District, Shanghai and Partnership Office of Network Hesse-China	Series activity
38	December 20-22	The 10th International Conference on Infrastructure Development of Underground Space	Underground Space-New Future of Urban Development	Baolong Hotel Shanghai	Tongji University, Shenzhen University, Shanghai Society of Civil Engineering, and Municipal Engineering Branch of China Civil Engineering Society	Series activity